$2.85

SPECIAL FUNCTIONS OF MATHEMATICAL
PHYSICS AND CHEMISTRY

UNIVERSITY MATHEMATICAL TEXTS

GENERAL EDITORS

ALEXANDER C. AITKEN, D.SC., F.R.S.
DANIEL E. RUTHERFORD, D.SC. DR.MATH.

SPECIAL FUNCTIONS OF MATHEMATICAL PHYSICS AND CHEMISTRY

IAN N. SNEDDON

M.A., D.Sc.

SIMSON PROFESSOR OF MATHEMATICS IN
THE UNIVERSITY OF GLASGOW

OLIVER AND BOYD
EDINBURGH AND LONDON
NEW YORK: INTERSCIENCE PUBLISHERS, INC.
1961

FIRST EDITION . . 1956
SECOND EDITION . 1961

PRINTED IN GREAT BRITAIN BY
OLIVER AND BOYD, LTD., EDINBURGH

PREFACE

THIS book is intended primarily for the student of applied mathematics, physics, chemistry or engineering who wishes to use the " special " functions associated with the names of Legendre, Bessel, Hermite and Laguerre. It aims at providing in a compact form most of the properties of these functions which arise most frequently in applications, and at establishing these properties in the simplest possible way. For that reason the methods it employs should be intelligible to anyone who has completed a first course in calculus and has a slight acquaintance with the theory of differential equations. Use is made of the theory of functions of a complex variable only very sparingly, and most of the book should be accessible to a reader who has no knowledge of this theory. Throughout the text an attempt is made to show how these functions may be used in the discussion of problems in classical physics and in quantum theory. A brief account is given in an appendix of the main properties of the Dirac delta " function ".

I should like to record my debt of gratitude to the late Sir John Lennard-Jones, and to my colleagues Mr. B. Noble and Dr. J. G. Clunie for their generous help in reading the first draft of the manuscript and making valuable suggestions for its improvement. I am indebted to Miss Janet Burchnall for her assistance in the preparation of the final manuscript, to Mr. J. S. Lowndes for help in correcting proof sheets and to Miss Elizabeth Gildart for preparing the index. I should also like to thank Dr. D. E. Rutherford, general editor of the series, for his advice and criticism throughout the preparation of the book.

My debt of gratitude to Professor T. M. MacRobert is a much more general one. It was at his lectures that I first acquired a taste for the subject, and it will be obvious to anyone who knows his published writings how much I have been influenced by them.

KEELE, STAFFORDSHIRE
20th August 1955

CONTENTS

CONTENTS

CHAPTER IV

BESSEL FUNCTIONS

CHAPTER V

THE FUNCTIONS OF HERMITE AND LAGUERRE

APPENDIX

THE DIRAC DELTA FUNCTION

CHAPTER I

INTRODUCTION

§ **1. The origin of special functions.** The special functions of mathematical physics arise in the solution of partial differential equations governing the behaviour of certain physical quantities. Probably the most frequently occurring equation of this type in all physics is Laplace's equation

$$\nabla^2 \psi = 0 \tag{1.1}$$

satisfied by a certain function ψ describing the physical situation under discussion. The mathematical problem consists of finding those functions which satisfy equation (1.1) and also satisfy certain prescribed conditions on the surfaces bounding the region being considered. For example, if ψ denotes the electrostatic potential of a system, ψ will be constant over any conducting surface. The shape of these boundaries often makes it desirable to work in curvilinear coordinates q_1, q_2, q_3 instead of in rectangular Cartesian coordinates x, y, z. In this case we have relations

$$x = x(q_1, q_2, q_3),\ y = y(q_1, q_2, q_3),\ z = z(q_1, q_2, q_3) \tag{1.2}$$

expressing the Cartesian coordinates in terms of the curvilinear coordinates. If equations (1.2) are such that

$$\frac{\partial x}{\partial q_i} \frac{\partial x}{\partial q_j} + \frac{\partial y}{\partial q_i} \frac{\partial y}{\partial q_j} + \frac{\partial z}{\partial q_i} \frac{\partial z}{\partial q_j} = 0$$

when $i \neq j$ we say that the coordinates q_1, q_2, q_3 are **orthogonal curvilinear coordinates.**† The element of

† D. E. Rutherford, *Vector Methods* (Oliver and Boyd, 1939), pp. 59-63.

length dl is then given by

$$dl^2 = h_1^2 \, dq_1^2 + h_2^2 \, dq_2^2 + h_3^2 \, dq_3^2 \tag{1.3}$$

where

$$h_i^2 = \left(\frac{\partial x}{\partial q_i}\right)^2 + \left(\frac{\partial y}{\partial q_i}\right)^2 + \left(\frac{\partial z}{\partial q_i}\right)^2 \tag{1.4}$$

and it can easily be shown that

$$\nabla^2 \psi = \frac{1}{h_1 h_2 h_3} \left\{ \frac{\partial}{\partial q_1}\left(\frac{h_2 h_3}{h_1} \frac{\partial \psi}{\partial q_1}\right) + \frac{\partial}{\partial q_2}\left(\frac{h_3 h_1}{h_2} \frac{\partial \psi}{\partial q_2}\right) \right. $$
$$\left. + \frac{\partial}{\partial q_3}\left(\frac{h_1 h_2}{h_3} \frac{\partial \psi}{\partial q_3}\right) \right\}. \tag{1.5}$$

One method of solving Laplace's equation consists of finding solutions of the type

$$\psi = Q_1(q_1) Q_2(q_2) Q_3(q_3)$$

by substituting from (1.5) into (1.1). We then find that

$$\frac{1}{Q_1} \frac{\partial}{\partial q_1}\left(\frac{h_2 h_3}{h_1} \frac{\partial Q_1}{\partial q_1}\right) + \frac{1}{Q_2} \frac{\partial}{\partial q_2}\left(\frac{h_3 h_1}{h_2} \frac{\partial Q_2}{\partial q_2}\right)$$
$$+ \frac{1}{Q_3} \frac{\partial}{\partial q_3}\left(\frac{h_1 h_2}{h_3} \frac{\partial Q_3}{\partial q_3}\right) = 0.$$

If, further, it so happens that

$$\frac{h_2 h_3}{h_1} = f_1(q_1) F_1(q_2, q_3)$$

etc., then this last equation reduces to the form

$$F_1(q_2, q_3) \frac{1}{Q_1} \frac{d}{dq_1}\left\{ f_1(q_1) \frac{dQ_1}{dq_1}\right\} +$$
$$+ F_2(q_3, q_1) \frac{1}{Q_2} \frac{d}{dq_2}\left\{ f_2(q_2) \frac{dQ_2}{dq_2}\right\}$$
$$+ F_3(q_1, q_2) \frac{1}{Q_3} \frac{d}{dq_3}\left\{ f_3(q_3) \frac{dQ_3}{dq_3}\right\} = 0.$$

Now, in certain circumstances, it is possible to find three functions $g_1(q_1)$, $g_2(q_2)$, $g_3(q_3)$ with the property that

$$F_1(q_2, q_3)g_1(q_1) + F_2(q_3, q_1)g_2(q_2) + F_3(q_1, q_2)g_3(q_3) \equiv 0.$$

When this is so, it follows immediately that the solution of Laplace's equation (1.1) reduces to the solution of three self-adjoint ordinary linear differential equations

$$\frac{d}{dq_i}\left\{f_i\frac{dQ_i}{dq_i}\right\} - g_iQ_i = 0, \quad (i = 1, 2, 3). \tag{1.6}$$

It is the study of differential equations of this kind which leads to the special functions of mathematical physics. The adjective " special " is used in this connection because here we are not, as in analysis, concerned with the general properties of functions, but only with the properties of functions which arise in the solution of special problems.

To take a particular case, consider the cylindrical polar coordinates (ϱ, ϕ, z) defined by the equations

$$x = \varrho \cos \phi, \ y = \varrho \sin \phi, \ z = z$$

for which $h_1 = 1$, $h_2 = \varrho$, $h_3 = 1$. From equation (1.5) we see that, for these coordinates, Laplace's equation is of the form

$$\frac{\partial^2\psi}{\partial\varrho^2} + \frac{1}{\varrho}\frac{\partial\psi}{\partial\varrho} + \frac{1}{\varrho^2}\frac{\partial^2\psi}{\partial\phi^2} + \frac{\partial^2\psi}{\partial z^2} = 0. \tag{1.7}$$

If we now make the substitution

$$\psi = R(\varrho)\Phi(\phi)Z(z), \tag{1.8}$$

we find that equation (1.7) may be written in the form

$$\frac{1}{R}\left(\frac{d^2R}{d\varrho^2} + \frac{1}{\varrho}\frac{dR}{d\varrho}\right) + \frac{1}{\varrho^2\Phi}\frac{d^2\Phi}{d\phi^2} + \frac{1}{Z}\frac{d^2Z}{dz^2} = 0.$$

This shows that if Φ, Z, R satisfy the equations

$$\frac{d^2\Phi}{d\phi^2} + n^2\Phi = 0, \tag{1.9a}$$

$$\frac{d^2Z}{dz^2} - m^2Z = 0, \tag{1.9b}$$

$$\frac{d^2R}{d\varrho^2} + \frac{1}{\varrho}\frac{dR}{d\varrho} + \left(m^2 - \frac{n^2}{\varrho^2}\right)R = 0 \tag{1.9c}$$

respectively, then the function (1.8) is a solution of Laplace's equation (1.7). The study of these ordinary differential equations will lead us to the special functions appropriate to this coordinate system. For instance, equation (1.9a) may be taken as the equation *defining* the circular functions. In this context $\sin(n\phi)$ is defined as that solution of (1.9a) which has value 0 when $\phi = 0$ and $\cos(n\phi)$ as that which has value 1 when $\phi = 0$ and the properties of the functions derived therefrom, cf. ex. 4 below. Similarly, equation (1.9b) defines the exponential functions. In actual practice we do not proceed in this way merely because we have already encountered these functions in another context and from their familiar properties studied their relation to equations (1.9a) and (1.9b). The situation with respect to equation (1.9c) is different; we cannot express its solution in terms of the elementary functions of analysis, as we were able to do with the other two equations. In this case we define new functions in terms of the solutions of this equation and by investigating the series solutions of the equations derive the properties of the functions so defined. Equation (1.9c) is called **Bessel's equation** and solutions of it are called **Bessel functions.** Bessel functions are of great importance in theoretical physics; they are discussed in Chapter IV below.

§ **2. Ordinary points of a linear differential equation.** We shall have occasion to discuss ordinary linear differential equations of the second order with variable coefficients whose solutions cannot be obtained in terms of the elementary functions of mathematical analysis. In such cases one of the standard procedures is to derive a pair of linearly independent solutions in the form of infinite series and from these series to compute tables of standard solutions. With the aid of such tables the solution appropriate to any given initial conditions may then be readily found. The object of this note is to outline briefly the procedure to be followed in these instances; for proofs of the theorems quoted the reader is referred to the standard textbooks.†

A function is called **analytic** at a point if it is possible to expand it in a Taylor series valid in some neighbourhood of the point. This is equivalent to saying that the function is single-valued and possesses derivatives of all orders at the point in question. In the equations we shall consider the coefficients will be analytic functions of the independent variable except possibly at certain isolated points.

An **ordinary** point $x = a$ of the second order differential equation

$$y'' + \alpha(x)y' + \beta(x)y = 0 \qquad (2.1)$$

is one at which the coefficients α, β are analytic functions. It can be shown that *at any ordinary point every solution of the equation is analytic.* Furthermore *if the Taylor expansions of $\alpha(x)$ and $\beta(x)$ are valid in the range $|x-a| < R$ the Taylor expansion of the solution is valid for the same range.* As a consequence, if $\alpha(x)$ and $\beta(x)$ are polynomials in x the series solution of (2.1) is valid for *all* values of x.

When, as is usually the case, $\alpha(x)$ and $\beta(x)$ are polynomials of low degree, the solution is most easily found by assuming a power series of the form

$$y = \sum_{r=0}^{\infty} c_r(x-a)^r \qquad (2.2)$$

for the solution and determining the coefficients $c_0, c_1, c_2, \ldots,$

† See, for example, E. L. Ince, *Ordinary Differential Equations*, (Longmans, 1927), Chap. VII; E. Goursat, *A Course in Mathematical Analysis*, Vol. II, Part II (Ginn, 1904), Chap. III; J. C. Burkill, *Theory of Ordinary Differential Equations* Chap. IV (Oliver and Boyd; 1956).

by direct substitution of (2.2) into (2.1) and equating coefficients of successive powers of x to zero.

The simplest equation of this type is

$$y'' + y = 0. \tag{2.3}$$

Substituting a solution of the type (2.2) with $a = 0$ into this equation we find that, if the equation is to be satisfied,

$$\sum_{r=0}^{\infty} r(r-1)c_r x^{r-2} + \sum_{r=0}^{\infty} c_r x^r = 0.$$

The series on the left is equivalent to

$$\sum_{r=0}^{\infty} (r+1)(r+2)c_{r+2} x^r$$

so that, equating coefficients of x^r, we see that the equation is satisfied by a solution of type (2.2) provided that the coefficients are connected by the relation

$$(r+1)(r+2)c_{r+2} + c_r = 0. \tag{2.4}$$

The coefficients c_0, c_1 are determined by the prescribed values of y, y' at $x = 0$, and the others are determined by equation (2.4). From this relation it follows that the solution is

$$y = c_0 \left(1 - \frac{x^2}{2!} + \frac{x^4}{4!} - \ldots\right) + c_1 \left(x - \frac{x^3}{3!} + \frac{x^5}{5!} - \ldots\right). \tag{2.5}$$

An equation of the kind (2.4) which determines the subsequent coefficients in terms of the first two is called a **recurrence relation**.

§ 3. **Regular singular points.**   If either of the functions $\alpha(x)$, $\beta(x)$ is not analytic at the point $x = a$, we say that this point is a **singular** point of the differential equation. When the functions $\alpha(x)$, $\beta(x)$ are of such a nature that the differential equation may be written in the form

$$(x-a)^2 y'' + (x-a)p(x)y' + q(x)y = 0 \tag{3.1}$$

where $p(x)$ and $q(x)$ are analytic at the point $x = a$ we say that this point is a **regular singular** point of the differential equation.

If $x = a$ is a regular singular point of the equation (3.1) it can be shown that there exists at least one solution of the form

$$y = \sum_{r=0}^{\infty} c_r(x-a)^{\varrho+r} \qquad (3.2)$$

which is valid in some neighbourhood of $x = a$. More specifically, if the Taylor expansions for $p(x)$, $q(x)$ are valid for $|x-a| < R$, the solution (3.2) is valid in the same range.

Putting

$$p(x) = \sum_{r=0}^{\infty} p_r(x-a)^r, \quad q(x) = \sum_{r=0}^{\infty} q_r(x-a)^r \quad (3.3)$$

and substituting the expansions (3.2) and (3.3) into (3.1) we see that for the equation (3.1) to be satisfied we must have

$$\sum_{r=0}^{\infty} c_r(\rho+r)(\rho+r-1)(x-a)^{\varrho+r}$$

$$+ \sum_{s=0}^{\infty} p_s(x-a)^s \sum_{r=0}^{\infty} c_r(\varrho+r)(x-a)^{\varrho+r}$$

$$+ \sum_{s=0}^{\infty} q_s(x-a)^s \sum_{r=0}^{\infty} c_r(x-a)^{\varrho+r} = 0. \qquad (3.4)$$

Equating to zero the coefficient of $(x-a)^\varrho$ we have the relation

$$c_0\varrho(\varrho-1) + p_0c_0\,\rho + q_0c_0 = 0$$

so that if $c_0 \neq 0$ we have the quadratic equation

$$\varrho^2 + (p_0-1)\varrho + q_0 = 0 \qquad (3.5)$$

for the determination of ϱ. This is known as the **indicial equation**. Similarly if we equate to zero the coefficient of

$(x-a)^{\varrho+r}$ we obtain the relation

$$c_r(\varrho+r)(\varrho+r-1)+\sum_{s=0}^{r}\{p_s(\varrho+r-s)+q_s\}c_{r-s}=0$$

which may be written in the form

$$c_r\{(\varrho+r)(\varrho+r-1)+p_0(\varrho+r)+q_0\}$$

$$+\sum_{s=1}^{r}\{p_s(\varrho+r-s)+q_s\}c_{r-s}=0. \qquad (3.6)$$

Equation (3.5) gives the two possible values ϱ_1, ϱ_2 of ϱ. If we take one of these values, ϱ_1 say, and substitute it in the **recurrence relation** (3.6) we obtain the corresponding value of the coefficients c_r and hence the solution

$$y_1(x) = \sum_{r=0}^{\infty} c_r(x-a)^{r+\varrho_1}.$$

In a similar way the root ϱ_2 of the indicial equation leads to the solution

$$y_2(x) = \sum_{r=0}^{\infty} c_r'(x-a)^{r+\varrho_2}.$$

Three distinct cases arise according to the nature of the roots of the indicial equation.

Case (i) $\varrho_1-\varrho_2$ *neither zero nor an integer*

In these circumstances the solutions $y_1(x)$ and $y_2(x)$ are linearly independent and the general solution of equation (3.1) is of the form

$$y = \sum_{r=0}^{\infty} c_r(x-a)^{r+\varrho_1}+ \sum_{r=0}^{\infty} c_r'(x-a)^{r+\varrho_2}. \qquad (3.7)$$

Case (ii) $\varrho_1 = \varrho_2$.

If $\varrho_1 = \varrho_2$ the solutions $y_1(x)$ and $y_2(x)$ are identical (except, possibly, for a multiplicative constant). The general solution of the equation can be shown to be

$y_1(x) + y_2(x)$ where

$$\left.\begin{array}{l} y_1(x) = (x-a)^{\varrho_1} \sum\limits_{r=0}^{\infty} c_r(x-a)^r, \\[2mm] y_2(x) = y_1(x) . \log(x-a) + (x-a)^{\varrho_1} \sum\limits_{r=0}^{\infty} \left(\dfrac{\partial c_r}{\partial \varrho}\right)_{\varrho=\varrho_1} (x-a)^r. \end{array}\right\} \quad (3.8)$$

Case (iii) $\varrho_2 = \varrho_1 - n$ *where n is a positive integer.*

In this case all the coefficients in one of the solutions from some point onwards are either infinite or indeterminate. It can be shown that the appropriate solutions are

$$\left.\begin{array}{l} y_1(x) = (x-a)^{\varrho_1} \sum\limits_{r=0}^{\infty} c_r(x-a)^r, \\[2mm] y_2(x) = g_n y_1(x) \log(x-a) + (x-a)^{\varrho_2} \sum\limits_{r=0}^{\infty} b_r(x-a)^r, \end{array}\right\} \quad (3.9)$$

where g_n is the coefficient of x^n in the expansion of

$$\frac{x^{n+1}}{\{y_1(x+a)\}^2} \exp\left[-\int_0^x u p(u) du\right].$$

It may happen that $g_n = 0$ in which case $y_2(x)$ does not contain a logarithmic term.

§ 4. The point at infinity.

In many problems we wish to find solutions of differential equations of the type (2.1) which are valid for large values of x. We seek solutions in the form of infinite series with variable $\dfrac{1}{x}$. If we make the transformation

$$x = \frac{1}{\xi}$$

the " point at infinity " is taken into the origin on the ξ-axis. With this change of variable equation (2.1) becomes

$$\frac{d^2y}{d\xi^2} + \left\{\frac{2}{\xi} - \frac{1}{\xi^2}\alpha\left(\frac{1}{\xi}\right)\right\}\frac{dy}{d\xi} + \frac{1}{\xi^4}\beta\left(\frac{1}{\xi}\right)y = 0. \quad (4.1)$$

B

If $2\xi^{-1} - \xi^{-2}\alpha(\xi^{-1})$, $\xi^{-4}\beta(\xi^{-1})$ are both $0(1)$ as $\xi \to 0$ and analytic in ξ then $\xi = 0$ is an ordinary point of equation (4.1) and we say that $x = \infty$ is an ordinary point of equation (2.1). Returning to the original independent variable we see that the conditions for the point at infinity to be an ordinary point of equation (2.1) are that

$$\alpha(x) = \frac{2}{x} + O(x^{-2}), \; \beta(x) = O(x^{-4}) \text{ as } x \to \infty. \quad (4.2)$$

The corresponding solutions are of the form

$$y = \sum_{r=0}^{\infty} c_r x^{-r}.$$

Similarly if, as $x \to \infty$

$$\alpha(x) = \frac{\alpha_0}{x} + O(x^{-2}), \quad \beta(x) = \frac{\beta_0}{x^2} + O(x^{-3}) \quad (4.3)$$

where α_0, β_0 are constants we say that the point at infinity is a regular singular point of the equation (2.1). The corresponding indicial equation is

$$\varrho^2 + (1-\alpha)\varrho + \beta = 0.$$

If the roots of this equation are ϱ_1, ϱ_2 the solutions of (2.1) valid for large values of x are of the form

$$y_1(x) = \sum_{r=0}^{\infty} c_r x^{-\varrho_1 - r}, \quad y_2(x) = \sum_{r=0}^{\infty} c_r' x^{-\varrho_2 - r}. \quad (4.4)$$

§ 5. The gamma function and related functions.

In developing series solutions of differential equations and in other formal calculations it is often convenient to make use of properties of gamma and beta functions. The integral

$$\Gamma(n) = \int_0^{\infty} e^{-x} x^{n-1} dx \quad (5.1)$$

converges if $n > 0$ and defines the **gamma function.** Similarly if $m > 0$, $n > 0$ the **beta function** is defined by the equation

$$B(m, n) = \int_0^1 x^{m-1}(1-x)^{n-1}dx. \tag{5.2}$$

It is then easily shown that †

  (i) $\Gamma(1) = 1$,

  (ii) $\Gamma(n+1) = n\Gamma(n)$,

  (iii) $\Gamma(n+1) = n!$ if n is a positive integer,

  (iv) $B(m, n) = 2\int_0^{\frac{1}{2}\pi} \sin^{2m-1}\theta \cos^{2n-1}\theta \, d\theta$,

  (v) $B(m, n) = \dfrac{\Gamma(m)\Gamma(n)}{\Gamma(m+n)}$,

  (vi) $\Gamma(\frac{1}{2}) = \sqrt{\pi}$,

  (vii) $\Gamma(p)\Gamma(1-p) = \pi \operatorname{cosec}(p\pi)$, $0 < p < 1$,

  (viii) $\Gamma(\frac{1}{2})\Gamma(2n) = 2^{2n-1}\Gamma(n)\Gamma(n+\frac{1}{2})$—the **duplication formula,**

  (ix) $\Gamma(z+1) = \lim\limits_{n\to\infty} \dfrac{n!\, n^z}{(z+1)(z+2)...(z+n)}$, $(z > 0)$.

When n is a negative fraction $\Gamma(n)$ is defined by means of equation (ii); for example

$$\Gamma(-\tfrac{3}{2}) = \frac{\Gamma(-\frac{1}{2})}{-\frac{3}{2}} = \frac{\Gamma(\frac{1}{2})}{(-\frac{3}{2})(-\frac{1}{2})} = \frac{4\Gamma(\frac{1}{2})}{3}.$$

By means of the result (ix) we can derive an interesting expression for **Euler's constant,** γ, which is defined by the equation

$$\gamma = \lim_{n\to\infty}\left(1 + \frac{1}{2} + ... + \frac{1}{n} - \log n\right) = 0.5772... \tag{5.3}$$

† For proofs of these results the reader is referred to R. P. Gillespie, *Integration* (Oliver and Boyd), 1951, pp. 90-95.

From (ix) we have

$$\frac{d}{dz}\{\log \Gamma(z+1)\} = \lim_{n\to\infty}\left(\log n - \frac{1}{z+1} - \frac{1}{z+2} - \ldots - \frac{1}{z+n}\right)$$

so that letting $z \to 0$ we obtain the result

$$\gamma = -\left[\frac{d}{dz}\log \Gamma(z+1)\right]_{z=0} \tag{5.4}$$

and from (5.1) we find

$$\gamma = -\int_0^\infty e^{-t}\log t\, dt \tag{5.5}$$

Integrating by parts we see that

$$\int_z^\infty e^{-t}\log t\, dt = +e^{-z}\log z + \int_z^\infty \frac{e^{-t}}{t}\, dt$$

so that

$$-\gamma = \lim_{z\to 0}\left(\int_z^\infty \frac{e^{-t}}{t}\, dt + \log z\right). \tag{5.6}$$

Closely related to the gamma function are the **exponential-integral** $\mathrm{ei}(x)$ defined by the equation

$$\mathrm{ei}(x) = \int_x^\infty \frac{e^{-u}}{u}\, du \quad (x>0), \tag{5.7}$$

and the **logarithmic-integral** $\mathrm{li}(x)$ defined by

$$\mathrm{li}(x) = \int_0^x \frac{du}{\log u}, \tag{5.8}$$

which are themselves connected by the relation

$$\mathrm{ei}(x) = -\mathrm{li}(e^{-x}). \tag{5.9}$$

Other integrals of importance are the **sine and cosine**

integrals Ci(x), Si(x), which are defined by the equations

$$\text{Ci}(x) = -\int_x^\infty \frac{\cos u}{u}\, du, \quad \text{Si}(x) = \int_0^x \frac{\sin u}{u}\, du \quad (5.10)$$

and whose variation with x is shown in Fig. 1.

In heat conduction problems solutions can often be expressed in terms of the **error-function**

$$\text{erf}(x) = \frac{2}{\sqrt{\pi}} \int_0^x e^{-u^2}\, du \quad (5.11)$$

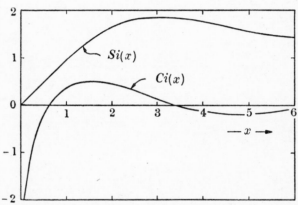

Fig. 1. Variation of Ci(x) and Si(x) with x.

whose variation with x is exhibited graphically in Fig. 2.†

Similarly in problems of wave motion the **Fresnel integrals**

$$C(x) = \int_0^x \cos\left(\tfrac{1}{2}\pi u^2\right) du, \quad S(x) = \int_0^x \sin\left(\tfrac{1}{2}\pi u^2\right) du \quad (5.12)$$

occur. The variation of these functions with x is shown in Fig. 3.

† A. C. Aitken, *Statistical Mathematics* (Oliver and Boyd, Seventh Edition, 1952), p. 62, gives a short table of values of erf (x).

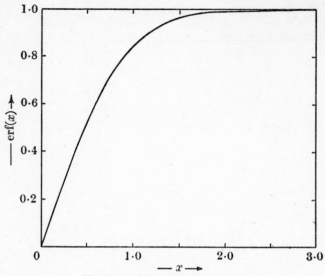

Fig. 2. Variation of erf(x) with x.

Fig. 3. Variation of the Fresnel integrals, C(x) and S(x), with x.

The importance of these functions lies in the fact that it is often possible to express solutions of physical problems in terms of them. The corresponding numerical values can then be obtained from works such as E. Jahnke and F. Emde, " *Funktionentafeln* " (Teubner, Leipzig, 1933) in which they are tabulated.

Examples I

(1) Show that, in spherical polar coordinates r, θ, ϕ defined by

$$x = r \sin \theta \cos \phi, \, y = r \sin \theta \sin \phi, \, z = r \cos \theta,$$

Laplace's equation becomes

$$\frac{\partial}{\partial r}\left(r^2 \frac{\partial \psi}{\partial r}\right) + \frac{1}{\sin \theta}\frac{\partial}{\partial \theta}\left(\sin \theta \frac{\partial \psi}{\partial \theta}\right) + \frac{1}{\sin^2 \theta}\frac{\partial^2 \psi}{\partial \psi^2} = 0,$$

and prove that it possesses solutions of the form $r^n e^{im\phi}\Theta$ $(\cos \theta)$, where $\Theta(\mu)$ satisfies the ordinary differential equation

$$(1-\mu^2)\frac{d^2\Theta}{d\mu^2} - 2\mu \frac{d\Theta}{d\mu} + \left\{n(n+1) - \frac{m^2}{1-\mu^2}\right\}\Theta = 0.$$

(2) Show that if

$$x = a \cosh \xi \cos \eta, \, y = a \sinh \xi \sin \eta, \, z = z$$

Laplace's equation assumes the form

$$\frac{\partial^2 \psi}{\partial \xi^2} + \frac{\partial^2 \psi}{\partial \eta^2} + a^2(\cosh^2 \xi - \cos^2 \eta)\frac{\partial^2 \psi}{\partial z^2} = 0.$$

Deduce that it has solutions of the form $f(i\xi)f(\eta)e^{-\gamma z}$ where $f(\eta)$ satisfies the equation

$$\frac{d^2f}{d\eta^2} + (G + 16q \cos 2\eta)f = 0$$

in which G is a constant of separation and $q = -a^2\gamma^2/32$.

(3) Parabolic coordinates ξ, η, ϕ are defined by

$$x = \sqrt{(\xi\eta)} \cos \phi, \, y = \sqrt{(\xi\eta)} \sin \phi, \, z = \tfrac{1}{2}(\xi - \eta).$$

Show that in these coordinates Laplace's equation becomes

$$\frac{4}{\xi+\eta} \frac{\partial}{\partial \xi} \left(\xi \frac{\partial \psi}{\partial \xi} \right) + \frac{4}{\xi+\eta} \frac{\partial}{\partial \eta} \left(\eta \frac{\partial \psi}{\partial \eta} \right) + \frac{1}{\xi\eta} \frac{\partial^2 \psi}{\partial \phi^2} = 0.$$

Prove that if $F_n(x)$ is a solution of the equation

$$x \frac{d^2 F}{dx^2} + \frac{dF}{dx} + \left(n - \frac{m^2}{4x} \right) F = 0$$

then $F_n(\xi) F_{-n}(\eta) e^{\pm im\phi}$ is a solution of Laplace's equation.

(4) Defining $\cos x$, $\sin x$ to be the solutions of

$$\frac{d^2 y}{dx^2} + y = 0$$

which respectively are 1, 0 when $x = 0$, prove

(i) $\cos(-x) = \cos x, \sin(-x) = -\sin x$;
(ii) $\cos(x+x') = \cos x \cos x' - \sin x \sin x'$;
(iii) $\sin(x+x') = \sin x \cos x' + \cos x \sin x'$;
(iv) $\cos^2 x + \sin^2 x = 1$;

(v) $\dfrac{d}{dx} (\sin x) = \cos x, \dfrac{d}{dx} (\cos x) = -\sin x.$

(5) The only singularities of the differential equation

$$y'' + p(x)y' + q(x)y = 0$$

are regular singularities at $x = 1$ of exponents α, α' and at $x = -1$ of exponents β, β' the point at infinity being an ordinary point. Prove that $\beta = -\alpha$, $\beta' = -\alpha'$ and that the differential equation is

$$(x^2-1)^2 y'' + 2(x-1)(x-\alpha-\alpha')y' + 4\alpha\alpha' y = 0.$$

Show that the solution is

$$y = c_1 \left(\frac{x-1}{x+1}\right)^{\alpha} + c_2 \left(\frac{x-1}{x+1}\right)^{\alpha'}$$

where c_1 and c_2 are constants.

(6) Apply the method of solution in series to the equation

$$x \frac{d^2y}{dx^2} + (a-x)\frac{dy}{dx} - y = 0$$

showing that, near $x = 0$, $y = Au + Bv$ where u is a Maclaurin series and $v = x^{1-a}e^x$. (a is not an integer.)

(7) Find two solutions of the equation

$$(x^2+2x)\frac{d^2y}{dx^2} + \frac{dy}{dx} - k(k+1)y = 0$$

in the form

$$y = \sum_{n=0}^{\infty} a_n x^{n+\varrho}.$$

Show that, if k is a positive integer, one of these solutions is the polynomial

$$1 + k(k+1)\sum_{n=1}^{k+1} \frac{(k+n-1)!}{(k-n+1)!}\frac{(2x)^n}{(2n)!}$$

(8) Prove that if s is an integer and a is fractional

$$\Gamma(a-s) = (-1)^s \frac{\Gamma(a)\Gamma(1-a)}{\Gamma(1-a+s)}.$$

(9) Show that

(i) $(\alpha-1)(\alpha)_{n-1} = (\alpha-1)_n$;

(ii) $(\alpha)_{n-r} = (-1)^r \frac{(\alpha)_n}{(1-\alpha-n)_r}$;

(iii) $\dfrac{n!}{(n-s)!} = (-1)^s(-n)_s;$

where

$$(\alpha)_r = \alpha(\alpha+1)(\alpha+2)\ldots(\alpha+r-1).$$

(10) Prove that

$$\mathrm{ei}(x) = -\gamma - \log x + x - \frac{x^2}{2.2!} + \frac{x^3}{3.3!} - \ldots$$

and deduce that

$$\mathrm{Ci}(x) = \gamma + \log x - \frac{x^2}{2.2!} + \frac{x^4}{4.4!} - \ldots,$$

$$\mathrm{Si}(x) = x - \frac{x^3}{3.3!} + \frac{x^5}{5.5!} - \ldots.$$

CHAPTER II

HYPERGEOMETRIC FUNCTIONS

§ 6. The hypergeometric series.

The series

$$1 + \frac{\alpha \cdot \beta}{1 \cdot \gamma} x + \frac{\alpha(\alpha+1)\beta(\beta+1)}{1 \cdot 2\gamma(\gamma+1)} x^2 + \dots \tag{6.1}$$

is of great importance in mathematics. Since it is an obvious generalisation of the geometric series

$$1 + x + x^2 + \dots,$$

it is called the **hypergeometric series.** It is readily shown that, provided γ is not zero or a negative integer, the series is absolutely convergent if $|x| > 1$, divergent if $|x| > 1$, while if $|x| = 1$ the series converges absolutely if $\gamma > \alpha + \beta$.† It is convergent when $x = -1$, provided that $\gamma > \alpha + \beta - 1$.

If we introduce the notation

$$(\alpha)_r = \alpha(\alpha+1)\dots(\alpha+r-1) = \frac{\Gamma(\alpha+r)}{\Gamma(\alpha)} \tag{6.2}$$

we may write the series (6.1) in the form

$$_2F_1(\alpha, \beta; \gamma; x) = \sum_{r=0}^{\infty} \frac{(\alpha)_r(\beta)_r}{r!(\gamma)_r} x^r, \tag{6.3}$$

the suffixes 2 and 1 denoting that there are two parameters of the type α and one of the type γ. We shall generalise

† See J. M. Hyslop, *Infinite Series*, Fifth Edition (Oliver and Boyd, 1954), p. 50.

this concept at a later stage (§ 12 below) but it is advisable at this stage to denote the "ordinary" hypergeometric function by the symbol $_2F_1$ instead of simply F, if we are to avoid confusion later. From the definition (6.3) it is obvious that

$$_2F_1(\beta, \alpha; \gamma; x) = {}_2F_1(\alpha, \beta; \gamma; x). \tag{6.4}$$

A significant property of the hypergeometric series follows immediately from the definition (6.3). We have

$$\frac{d}{dx} {}_2F_1(\alpha, \beta; \gamma; x) = \sum_{r=1}^{\infty} \frac{(\alpha)_r(\beta)_r}{(r-1)!(\gamma)_r} x^{r-1}$$

$$= \sum_{r=0}^{\infty} \frac{(\alpha)_{r+1}(\beta)_{r+1}}{r!(\gamma)_{r+1}} x^r.$$

Now $(\alpha)_{r+1} = \alpha(\alpha+1)_r$ so the right-hand side of the last equation becomes

$$\frac{\alpha\beta}{\gamma} \sum_{r=0}^{\infty} \frac{(\alpha+1)_r(\beta+1)_r}{r!(\gamma+1)_r} x^r$$

showing that

$$\frac{d}{dx} {}_2F_1(\alpha, \beta; \gamma; x) = \frac{\alpha\beta}{\gamma} {}_2F_1(\alpha+1, \beta+1; \gamma+1; x). \tag{6.5}$$

It should also be observed that

$$_2F_1(\alpha, \beta; \gamma; 0) = 1 \tag{6.6}$$

so that

$$\left[\frac{d}{dx} {}_2F_1(\alpha, \beta; \gamma; x) \right]_{x=0} = \frac{\alpha\beta}{\gamma}. \tag{6.7}$$

Several well-known elementary functions can be expressed as hypergeometric series; examples of them are given in ex. 1 below.

It should be noted that, if we adopt a certain convention, a hypergeometric series can stop and start again after a number of zero terms. For example, consider the hyper-geometric series $_2F_1(-n; \ b; \ -n-m; \ x)$ where both m and n are positive integers and b is neither zero nor a negative integer. Because of the occurrence of $(-n)_r$ in the numerator in the expansion in powers of x it is obvious that the $(n+1)$th term of the expansion will be zero, and we are tempted to think that every subsequent term is also zero. If we note that, as a result of ex. 9 (iii) of Chapter I,

$$\frac{(-n)_r}{(-n-m)_r} = \frac{n!}{(n+m)!} (n+m-r)(n+m-r-1)...(n-r+1)$$

$$(6.8)$$

when the form on the left is not of type $0/0$, and if, further, we assume that it still has the value on the left when it is indeterminate, we see that we may write

$$_2F_1(-n, \ b; \ -n-m; \ x)$$

$$= \sum_{r=0}^{\infty} \left(1 - \frac{r}{n+m}\right)\left(1 - \frac{r}{n+m-1}\right)...\left(1 - \frac{r}{n+1}\right) \frac{(b)_r x^r}{r!}, \ (6.9)$$

so that although the series stops at the nth term it starts up again at the $(n+m+1)$th term. For instance,

$$_2F_1(-2, 1; \ -5; \ x)$$

$$= 1 + \frac{2}{5}x + \frac{1}{10}x^2 - \frac{1}{10}x^6 - \frac{2}{5}x^7 - x^8 + ...$$

According to a different convention, however, the hypergeometric function does not restart after a set of zero terms.

§ 7. An integral formula for the hypergeometric series.
In order to derive some further properties of the hyper-geometric series we shall first of all establish an expression for the series in the form of an integral. It is readily shown

that

$$\frac{(\beta)_r}{(\gamma)_r} = \frac{B(\beta+r, \gamma-\beta)}{B(\beta, \gamma-\beta)} = \frac{1}{B(\beta, \gamma-\beta)} \int_0^1 (1-t)^{\gamma-\beta-1} t^{\beta+r-1} \, dt$$

from which it follows that

$$_2F_1(\alpha, \beta; \gamma; x)$$
$$= \frac{1}{B(\beta, \gamma-\beta)} \sum_{r=0}^{\infty} \frac{(\alpha)_r}{r!} x^r \int_0^1 (1-t)^{\gamma-\beta-1} t^{\beta+r-1} \, dt.$$

Interchanging the order in which the operations of summation and integration are performed we see that

$$_2F_1(\alpha, \beta; \gamma; x)$$
$$= \frac{1}{B(\beta, \gamma-\beta)} \int_0^1 (1-t)^{\gamma-\beta-1} t^{\beta-1} \left\{ \sum_{r=0}^{\infty} \frac{(\alpha)_r}{r!} (xt)^r \right\} \, dt.$$

Using the fact that

$$\sum_{r=0}^{\infty} \frac{(\alpha)_r}{r!} (xt)^r = (1-xt)^{-\alpha},$$

we have the integral formula

$$_2F_1(\alpha, \beta; \gamma; x)$$
$$= \frac{1}{B(\beta, \gamma-\beta)} \int_0^1 (1-t)^{\gamma-\beta-1} t^{\beta-1} (1-xt)^{-\alpha} \, dt, \quad (7.1)$$

valid if $|x| < 1$, $\gamma > \beta > 0$. The results hold if x is complex provided that we choose the branch of $(1-xt)^{-\alpha}$ in such a way that $(1-xt)^{-\alpha} \to 1$ as $t \to 0$ and $\mathscr{R}(\gamma) > \mathscr{R}(\beta) > 0$.

The first application of (7.1) is the derivation of the value of the hypergeometric series with unit argument. Putting $x = 1$ in (7.1) we have

$$_2F_1(\alpha, \beta; \gamma; 1) = \frac{1}{B(\beta, \gamma-\beta)} \int_0^1 (1-t)^{\gamma-\alpha-\beta-1} t^{\beta-1} \, dt$$
$$= \frac{B(\beta, \gamma-\alpha-\beta)}{B(\beta, \gamma-\beta)}$$

if $\gamma - \alpha - \beta > 0$, $\beta > 0$. If we express the beta function in terms of gamma functions we have **Gauss's Theorem**

$$_2F_1(\alpha, \beta; \gamma; 1) = \frac{\Gamma(\gamma)\Gamma(\gamma - \alpha - \beta)}{\Gamma(\gamma - \alpha)\Gamma(\gamma - \beta)}. \tag{7.2}$$

Now if $\alpha = -n$, a negative integer, we have

$$\frac{\Gamma(\gamma - \alpha - \beta)}{\Gamma(\gamma - \beta)} = (\gamma - \beta)_n, \quad \frac{\Gamma(\gamma - \alpha)}{\Gamma(\gamma)} = (\gamma)_n$$

so that equation (7.2) reduces to

$$_2F_1(-n, \beta; \gamma; 1) = \frac{(\gamma - \beta)_n}{(\gamma)_n}$$

which is known, in elementary mathematics, as **Vandermonde's theorem**.

Again, if we put $x = -1$ and $\alpha = 1 + \beta - \gamma$ we have, from equation (7.1)

$$_2F_1(\alpha, \beta; \beta - \alpha + 1; -1) = \frac{\Gamma(1 + \beta - \alpha)}{\Gamma(\beta)\Gamma(1 - \alpha)} \int_0^1 (1 - t^2)^{-\alpha} t^{\beta - 1} \, dt.$$

If we write $\xi = t^2$ in this integral we see that its value is $\frac{1}{2} B(\frac{1}{2}\beta, 1 - \alpha)$. Using this result and the relation $\frac{1}{2}\Gamma(\frac{1}{2}\beta)/\Gamma(\beta) = \Gamma(1 + \frac{1}{2}\beta)/\Gamma(1 + \beta)$ we have **Kummer's theorem**

$$_2F_1(\alpha, \beta, \beta - \alpha + 1; -1) = \frac{\Gamma(1 + \beta - \alpha)\Gamma(1 + \frac{1}{2}\beta)}{\Gamma(1 + \beta)\Gamma(1 + \frac{1}{2}\beta - \alpha)}. \tag{7.3}$$

Further, we can deduce from the formula (7.1) relations between hypergeometric series of argument x and those of argument $x/(x-1)$. Putting $\tau = 1 - t$ in equation (7.1), and noting that

$$\{1 - x(1 - \tau)\}^{-\alpha} = (1 - x)^{-\alpha} \left\{1 - \frac{x}{x - 1}\tau\right\}^{-\alpha},$$

we see that

$$_2F_1(\alpha, \beta; \gamma; x)$$

$$= \frac{(1-x)^{-\alpha}}{B(\beta, \gamma-\beta)} \int_0^1 (1-\tau)^{\beta-1} \tau^{\gamma-\beta-1} \left\{1 - \frac{x}{x-1}\tau\right\}^{-\alpha} d\tau$$

$$= \frac{(1-x)^{-\alpha}}{B(\beta, \gamma-\beta)} B(\gamma-\beta, \beta) \, _2F_1\left(\alpha, \gamma-\beta; \gamma; \frac{x}{x-1}\right),$$

whence we have the relation

$$_2F_1(\alpha, \beta; \gamma; x) = (1-x)^{-\alpha} \, _2F_1\left(\alpha, \gamma-\beta; \gamma; \frac{x}{x-1}\right), \quad (7.4)$$

and, by symmetry, the relation

$$_2F_1(\alpha, \beta; \gamma; x) = (1-x)^{-\beta} \, _2F_1\left(\gamma-\alpha, \beta; \gamma; \frac{x}{x-1}\right). \quad (7.5)$$

Using the symmetry relation (6.4) and equation (7.4) with x replaced by $x/(x-1)$ we see that

$$_2F_1\left(\alpha, \gamma-\beta; \gamma; \frac{x}{x-1}\right) = \, _2F_1\left(\gamma-\beta, \alpha; \gamma; \frac{x}{x-1}\right)$$

$$= (1-x)^{\gamma-\beta} \, _2F_1(\gamma-\beta, \gamma-\alpha; \gamma; x),$$

so that

$$_2F_1(\alpha, \beta; \gamma; x) = (1-x)^{\gamma-\alpha-\beta} \, _2F_1(\gamma-\alpha, \gamma-\beta; \gamma; x). \quad (7.6)$$

If we put $x = \frac{1}{2}$ in equation (7.4) we obtain the relation

$$_2F_1(\alpha, \beta; \gamma; \tfrac{1}{2}) = 2^{\alpha} \, _2F_1(\alpha, \gamma-\beta; \gamma; -1).$$

The series on the right-hand side of this equation can be derived from equation (7.3) provided either that

$$\gamma = \gamma-\beta-\alpha+1, \text{ i.e. } \beta = 1-\alpha,$$

or that

$$\gamma = \alpha-(\gamma-\beta)+1, \text{ i.e. } \gamma = \tfrac{1}{2}(\alpha+\beta+1).$$

We then obtain the formulae

$$_2F_1(\alpha, 1-\alpha; \gamma; \tfrac{1}{2}) = \frac{\Gamma(\tfrac{1}{2}\gamma)\Gamma(\tfrac{1}{2}\gamma+\tfrac{1}{2})}{\Gamma(\tfrac{1}{2}\alpha+\tfrac{1}{2}\gamma)\Gamma(\tfrac{1}{2}-\tfrac{1}{2}\alpha+\tfrac{1}{2}\gamma)}; \qquad (7.7)$$

$$_2F_1(\alpha, \beta; \tfrac{1}{2}\alpha+\tfrac{1}{2}\beta+\tfrac{1}{2}; \tfrac{1}{2}) = \frac{\Gamma(\tfrac{1}{2})\Gamma(\tfrac{1}{2}+\tfrac{1}{2}\alpha+\tfrac{1}{2}\beta)}{\Gamma(\tfrac{1}{2}+\tfrac{1}{2}\alpha)\Gamma(\tfrac{1}{2}+\tfrac{1}{2}\beta)}. \qquad (7.8)$$

§ 8. The hypergeometric equation.

In certain problems it is possible to reduce the solution to that of solving the second order linear differential equation

$$x(1-x)\frac{d^2y}{dx^2} + \{\gamma-(1+\alpha+\beta)x\}\frac{dy}{dx} - \alpha\beta y = 0 \qquad (8.1)$$

in which α, β and γ are constants. For instance, the Schrödinger equation for a symmetrical-top molecule, which is of importance in the theory of molecular spectra,[†] can, by simple transformations, be reduced to this type. An equation of this type also arises in the study of the flow of compressible fluids. In addition certain other differential equations (such as that occurring in ex. 1 of Chapter I) which arise in the solution of boundary value problems in mathematical physics can, by a simple change of variable, be transformed to an equation of type (8.1). Indeed it can be shown that any ordinary linear differential equation of the second order whose only singular points are regular singular points, one of which may be the point at infinity, can be transformed to the form (8.1). For that reason it is desirable to investigate the nature of the solutions of this equation, which is called the **hypergeometric equation.**

We may write the hypergeometric equation in the form

$$x^2y'' + x(1+x+x^2+\ldots)\{\gamma-(\alpha+\beta+1)x\}y'$$
$$-\alpha\beta x(1+x+x^2+\ldots)y = 0,$$

† See, for example, L. Pauling and E. B. Wilson, *Introduction to Quantum Mechanics, with Applications to Chemistry* (McGraw-Hill, New York, 1935), pp. 275-280, and ex. 10 below.

c

so that, in the notation of § 3, we see that near $x = 0$

$$p_0 = \gamma, \quad q_0 = 0,$$

and the indicial equation is

$$\varrho^2 + (\gamma - 1)\varrho = 0$$

with roots $\varrho = 0$ and $\varrho = 1 - \gamma$.

Similarly, the equation can be put in the form

$$(x - 1)^2 y'' - (x-1)\{\gamma - \alpha - \beta - 1 - \gamma(x-1) + \ldots\}y'$$
$$+ \alpha\beta(x-1)\{1 - (x-1) + \ldots\}y = 0,$$

with indicial equation

$$\varrho^2 + (\alpha + \beta - \gamma)\varrho = 0,$$

of which the roots are $\varrho = 0$, $\varrho = \gamma - \alpha - \beta$.

Finally in the notation of § 4 we have for large values of x

$$\alpha(x) \sim \frac{(\alpha + \beta + 1)}{x}, \quad \beta(x) \sim \frac{\alpha\beta}{x^2}$$

and so the indicial equation appropriate to the point at infinity is

$$\varrho^2 - (\alpha + \beta)\varrho + \alpha\beta = 0,$$

with roots α, β.

Thus the regular singular points of the hypergeometric equation are:—

  (i) $x = 0$ with exponents $0, 1 - \gamma$;
  (ii) $x = \infty$ with exponents α, β;
  (iii) $x = 1$ with exponents $0, \gamma - \alpha - \beta$.

These facts are exhibited symbolically by denoting the most general solution of the hypergeometric equation by a scheme of the form

$$y = P \left\{ \begin{array}{ccc} 0 & \infty & 1 \\ 0 & \alpha & 0 \\ 1 - \gamma & \beta & \gamma - \alpha - \beta \end{array} \ x \right\}. \tag{8.2}$$

The symbol on the right is called the **Riemann-P-function** of the equation.

We shall now consider the form of the solutions in the neighbourhood of the regular singular points.

(a) $x = 0$: Corresponding to the root $\varrho = 0$ we have a solution of the form

$$y = \sum_{r=0}^{\infty} c_r x^r.$$

Substituting this series into equation (8.1) we obtain the relation

$$(1-x) \sum_{r=0}^{\infty} c_r r(r-1) x^{r-1}$$
$$+ \{\gamma - (\alpha+\beta+1)x\} \sum_{r=0}^{\infty} c_r r x^{r-1} - \alpha\beta \sum_{r=0}^{\infty} c_r x^r = 0$$

which is readily seen to be equivalent to

$$\sum_{r=0}^{\infty} \{c_{r+1}[r(r+1)+(r+1)\gamma] - c_r(r+\alpha)(r+\beta)\} x^r = 0,$$

so that

$$c_{r+1} = \frac{(r+\alpha)(r+\beta)}{(r+1)(r+\gamma)} c_r, \qquad (8.3)$$

from which it follows that

$$c_r = \frac{(\alpha)_r (\beta)_r}{(\gamma)_r r!} c_0. \qquad (8.4)$$

It follows that the solution which reduces to unity when $x = 0$ is

$$y = 1 + \frac{\alpha\beta}{\gamma 1!} x + \frac{\alpha(\alpha+1)\beta(\beta+1)}{\gamma(\gamma+1)2!} x^2 + \dots$$

i.e. $$y = {}_2F_1(\alpha, \beta; \gamma; x). \qquad (8.5)$$

Similarly, if $1-\gamma$ is not zero nor a positive nor negative integer, the solution corresponding to the root $\varrho = 1-\gamma$ is

$$y = \sum_{r=0}^{\infty} c_r x^{1-\gamma+r}$$

where

$$(1-x) \sum_{r=0}^{\infty} c_r(r+1-\gamma)(r-\gamma)x^{r-\gamma} +$$

$$+ \{\gamma-(\alpha+\beta+1)x\} \sum_{r=0}^{\infty} c_r(r+1-\gamma)x^{r-\gamma} - \alpha\beta \sum_{r=0}^{\infty} c_r x^{1-\gamma+r} = 0,$$

which is equivalent to

$$\sum_{r=0}^{\infty} c_r\{(r+1-\gamma)(r-\gamma)+\gamma(r+1-\gamma)\}x^{r-\gamma} -$$

$$- \sum_{r=0}^{\infty} c_r\{(r+1-\gamma)(r-\gamma)+(\alpha+\beta+1)(r+1-\gamma)+\alpha\beta\}x^{r-\gamma+1} = 0,$$

implying that

$$c_{r+1} = \frac{(r+\alpha-\gamma+1)(r+\beta-\gamma+1)}{(r+1)(r+2-\gamma)} c_r.$$

Comparing this relation with (8.3) and taking $c_0 = 1$ we see that this solution is

$$x^{1-\gamma} {}_2F_1(\alpha-\gamma+1, \beta-\gamma+1; 2-\gamma; x). \tag{8.6}$$

Combining equations (8.5) and (8.6) we see that the general solution valid in the neighbourhood of the origin is

$$y = A \, {}_2F_1(\alpha, \beta; \gamma; x)$$

$$+ Bx^{1-\gamma} {}_2F_1(\alpha-\gamma+1, \beta-\gamma+1; 2-\gamma; x), \tag{8.7}$$

provided that $1-\gamma$ is not zero or a positive integer.

If $\gamma = 1$, the solutions (8.5) and (8.6) are identical. If we write

$$y_1(x) = {}_2F_1(\alpha, \beta; \gamma; x)$$

and put

$$y_2(x) = y_1(x) \log x + \sum_{r=1}^{\infty} c_r x^r$$

we find on substituting in (8.1), with $\gamma = 1$, that

$$(r+1)^2 c_{r+1} - r(\alpha+\beta+1)c_r + \frac{(\alpha)_r(\beta)_r(\alpha\beta-\alpha-\beta-r)}{r!(r+1)!} = 0$$

from which the coefficients c_r may be determined.

A similar procedure holds when $1-\gamma$ is a positive integer.

(b) $x = 1$: If we let $\xi = 1-x$, equation (8.1) reduces to

$$\xi(1-\xi)\frac{d^2y}{d\xi^2} + \{\alpha+\beta-\gamma+1-(\alpha+\beta+1)\xi\}\frac{dy}{d\xi} - \alpha\beta y = 0$$

which is identical with equation (8.1) with γ replaced by $\alpha+\beta-\gamma+1$, and x by $\xi = 1-x$. Hence it follows from equation (8.7) that the required solution is

$$y = A\ _2F_1(\alpha, \beta; \alpha+\beta-\gamma+1; 1-x)$$
$$+ B(1-x)^{\gamma-\alpha-\beta}\ _2F_1(\gamma-\alpha, \gamma-\beta; \gamma-\alpha-\beta+1; 1-x). \quad (8.8)$$

(c) $x = \infty$: Corresponding to the root $\varrho = \alpha$, we put

$$y = \sum_{r=0}^{\infty} c_r x^{-\alpha-r},$$

which gives

$$(1-x)\sum_{r=0}^{\infty} c_r(r+\alpha)(r+\alpha+1)x^{-r-\alpha-1}$$

$$-\{\gamma-(\alpha+\beta+1)x\}\sum_{r=0}^{\infty}(r+\alpha)c_r x^{-r-\alpha-1} - \alpha\beta\sum_{r=0}^{\infty}c_r x^{-r-\alpha} = 0,$$

i.e.,

$$\sum_{r=0}^{\infty} c_r(r+\alpha)(r+\alpha-\gamma+1)x^{-r-\alpha-1} = \sum_{r=0}^{\infty} c_r r(r+\alpha-\beta)x^{-r-\alpha},$$

whence it follows that

$$c_{r+1} = \frac{(r+\alpha)(r+\alpha-\gamma+1)}{(r+1)(r+\alpha-\beta+1)}\ c_r,$$

which in turn is equivalent to

$$c_r = \frac{(\alpha)_r(\alpha-\gamma+1)_r}{r!(\alpha-\beta+1)_r}\, c_0.$$

Taking $c_0 = 1$ we obtain the solution

$$x^{-\alpha}\, {}_2F_1\left(\alpha,\, \alpha-\gamma+1;\, \alpha-\beta+1;\, \frac{1}{x}\right).$$

From the symmetry we see that the other solution is

$$x^{-\beta}\, {}_2F_1\left(\beta,\, \beta-\gamma+1;\, \beta-\alpha+1;\, \frac{1}{x}\right),$$

so that the required solution is

$$y = Ax^{-\alpha}\, {}_2F_1\left(\alpha,\, \alpha-\gamma+1;\, \alpha-\beta+1;\, \frac{1}{x}\right)$$
$$+ Bx^{-\beta}\, {}_2F_1\left(\beta,\, \beta-\gamma+1;\, \beta-\alpha+1;\, \frac{1}{x}\right). \tag{8.9}$$

§ 9. **Linear relations between the solutions of the hypergeometric equation.**   The series in the solution (8.7) are convergent if $|x| < 1$, i.e. in the interval $(-1,\, 1)$ whereas those in the solution (8.8) are convergent in $(0,\, 2)$. There is therefore an interval, namely $(0,\, 1)$, in which all four series converge, and since only two solutions of the differential equation are linearly independent it follows that there must be a linear relation, valid if $0 < x < 1$, between solutions of type (8.7) and those of type (8.8).

Let

$${}_2F_1(\alpha,\, \beta;\, \gamma;\, x) = A\,{}_2F_1(\alpha,\, \beta;\, \alpha+\beta-\gamma+1;\, 1-x)$$
$$+ B(1-x)^{\gamma-\alpha-\beta}\, {}_2F_1(\gamma-\alpha,\, \gamma-\beta;\, \gamma-\alpha-\beta+1;\, 1-x),$$

then putting $x = 0$ we have

$$1 = A \,_2F_1(\alpha, \beta; \alpha+\beta-\gamma+1; 1)$$
$$+ B \,_2F_1(\gamma-\alpha, \gamma-\beta; \gamma-\alpha-\beta+1; 1),$$

and putting $x = 1$ we have

$$_2F_1(\alpha, \beta; \gamma; 1) = A,$$

if we assume that

$$1 > \gamma > \alpha+\beta. \tag{9.1}$$

Substituting for the series with unit argument from equation (7.2) we see that

$$A = \frac{\Gamma(\gamma)\Gamma(\gamma-\alpha-\beta)}{\Gamma(\gamma-\alpha)\Gamma(\gamma-\beta)},$$

and that

$$1 = A \frac{\Gamma(\alpha+\beta-\gamma+1)\Gamma(1-\gamma)}{\Gamma(\beta-\gamma+1)\Gamma(\alpha-\gamma+1)} + B \frac{\Gamma(\gamma-\alpha-\beta+1)\Gamma(1-\gamma)}{\Gamma(1-\beta)\Gamma(1-\alpha)},$$

so that

$$B = \frac{\Gamma(\gamma)\Gamma(\alpha+\beta-\gamma)}{\Gamma(\alpha)\Gamma(\beta)},$$

whence we find that

$$_2F_1(\alpha, \beta; \gamma; x)$$
$$= \frac{\Gamma(\gamma)\Gamma(\gamma-\alpha-\beta)}{\Gamma(\gamma-\alpha)\Gamma(\gamma-\beta)} \,_2F_1(\alpha, \beta; \alpha+\beta-\gamma+1; 1-x)$$
$$+ \frac{\Gamma(\gamma)\Gamma(\alpha+\beta-\gamma)}{\Gamma(\alpha)\Gamma(\beta)} (1-x)^{\gamma-\alpha-\beta}$$
$$_2F_1(\gamma-\alpha, \gamma-\beta; \gamma-\alpha-\beta+1; 1-x), \tag{9.2}$$

provided that the condition (9.1) is satisfied and $0 < x < 1$.

If we replace x by $\dfrac{1}{x}$ in equation (9.2) we have

$$
{}_2F_1\left(\alpha,\,\beta;\,\gamma;\,\frac{1}{x}\right)
$$

$$
= \frac{\Gamma(\gamma)\Gamma(\gamma-\alpha-\beta)}{\Gamma(\gamma-\alpha)\Gamma(\gamma-\beta)}\,{}_2F_1\left(\alpha,\,\beta;\,\alpha+\beta-\gamma+1;\,1-\frac{1}{x}\right)
$$

$$
+ \frac{\Gamma(\gamma)\Gamma(\alpha+\beta-\gamma)}{\Gamma(\alpha)\Gamma(\beta)}\left(1-\frac{1}{x}\right)^{\gamma-\alpha-\beta}
$$

$$
{}_2F_1\left(\gamma-\alpha,\,\gamma-\beta;\,\gamma-\alpha-\beta+1;\,1-\frac{1}{x}\right),
$$

and from equation (7.4)

$$
{}_2F_1\left(\alpha,\,\beta;\,\gamma;\,1-\frac{1}{x}\right) = x^{\alpha}\,{}_2F_1(\alpha,\,\gamma-\beta;\,\gamma;\,1-x),
$$

so that

$$
F\left(\alpha,\,\beta;\,\gamma;\,\frac{1}{x}\right)
$$

$$
= \frac{\Gamma(\gamma)\Gamma(\gamma-\alpha-\beta)}{\Gamma(\gamma-\alpha)\Gamma(\gamma-\beta)}\,x^{\alpha}\,{}_2F_1(\alpha,\,\alpha-\gamma+1;\,\alpha+\beta-\gamma+1;\,1-x)
$$

$$
+ \frac{\Gamma(\gamma)\Gamma(\alpha+\beta-\gamma)}{\Gamma(\alpha)\Gamma(\beta)}\,x^{\beta}(x-1)^{\gamma-\alpha-\beta}
$$

$$
{}_2F_1(\gamma-\alpha,\,1-\alpha;\,\gamma-\alpha-\beta+1;\,1-x), \quad (9.3)
$$

where $1<x<2$ and $1>\gamma>\alpha+\beta$.

These relations are typical of a larger number which exist between the solutions of the hypergeometric equation (8.1). If we change the independent variable in this equation to any one of

$$
1-x,\ \frac{1}{x},\ \frac{1}{1-x},\ \frac{x-1}{x},\ \frac{x}{x-1}
$$

the equation transforms to one of the same type (but, of course, with different parameters). The equation (8.1) therefore has twelve solutions of the types (8.5) and (8.6) —two for each independent variable—each convergent within the unit circle. Any one of these can be expressed in terms of two fundamental solutions. In addition twelve more solutions of the kinds

$$(1-x)^{\gamma-\alpha-\beta}\,_2F_1(\gamma-\alpha,\ \gamma-\beta;\ \gamma;\ x),$$
$$x^{1-\gamma}(1-x)^{\gamma-\alpha-\beta}\,_2F_1(1-\alpha,\ 1-\beta;\ 2-\gamma;\ x)$$

can be derived. The relations between these twenty-four solutions of the hypergeometric equation are of the types (9.2) and (9.3); for a full discussion of them the reader is referred to T. M. MacRobert, *Functions of a Complex Variable* (Macmillan, 2nd edition), pp. 298-301.

§ **10. Relations of contiguity.** Certain simple relations exist between hypergeometric functions whose parameters differ by ± 1. For example if the parameters α and β remain fixed and γ is varied we can prove that

$$\gamma\{\gamma-1-(2\gamma-1-\alpha-\beta)x\}\,_2F_1(\alpha,\ \beta;\ \gamma;\ x)$$
$$+(\gamma-\alpha)(\gamma-\beta)x\,_2F_1(\alpha,\ \beta;\ \gamma+1;\ x)$$
$$-\gamma(\gamma-1)(1-x)\,_2F_1(\alpha,\ \beta;\ \gamma-1;\ x)=0. \qquad (10.1)$$

The proof follows from the definition (6.3). For the coefficient of x^n in the expansion of the function on the left of (10.1) is

$$\gamma(\gamma-1)\frac{(\alpha)_n(\beta)_n}{(\gamma)_n n!}-(2\gamma-\alpha-\beta)\frac{(\alpha)_{n-1}(\beta)_{n-1}}{(\gamma)_{n-1}(n-1)!}$$
$$+(\gamma-\alpha)(\gamma-\beta)\frac{(\alpha)_{n-1}(\beta)_{n-1}}{(\gamma+1)_{n-1}(n-1)!}-\gamma(\gamma-1)\frac{(\alpha)_n(\beta)_n}{(\gamma-1)_n n!}$$
$$+\gamma(\gamma-1)\frac{(\alpha)_{n-1}(\beta)_{n-1}}{(\gamma-1)_{n-1}(n-1)!}$$

and it is not difficult to show that this is zero.

In another kind β and γ are kept constant and α is varied. One such is

$$\{\gamma-\alpha-\beta+(\beta-\alpha)(1-x)\}\,_2F_1(\alpha,\,\beta;\,\gamma;\,x)$$
$$+\alpha(1-x)\,_2F_1(\alpha+1,\,\beta;\,\gamma;\,x)-(\gamma-\alpha)\,_2F_1(\alpha-1,\,\beta;\,\gamma;\,x)=0$$
$$(10.2)$$

the proof of which is similarly direct.

In the third type of relation γ is kept constant and α and β vary. One of the simplest among these relations is

$$(\alpha-\beta)\,_2F_1(\alpha,\,\beta;\,\gamma;\,x)=\alpha\,_2F_1(\alpha+1,\,\beta;\,\gamma;\,x)$$
$$-\beta\,_2F_1(\alpha,\,\beta+1;\,\gamma;\,x)\qquad(10.3)$$

The proof of these relations is left to the reader; further examples are given below (exs. 3, 4).

§ 11. The confluent hypergeometric function.

If we replace x by x/β in equation (8.1) we see that the hypergeometric function

$$_2F_1(\alpha,\,\beta;\,\gamma;\,x/\beta)$$

is a solution of the differential equation

$$x\left(1-\frac{x}{\beta}\right)\frac{d^2y}{dx^2}+\left\{\gamma-\left(1+\frac{\alpha+1}{\beta}\right)x\right\}\frac{dy}{dx}-\alpha y=0$$

so that letting $\beta\to\infty$ we see that the function

$$\lim_{\beta\to\infty}\,_2F_1(\alpha,\,\beta;\,\gamma;\,x/\beta)\qquad(11.1)$$

is a solution of the differential equation

$$x\frac{d^2y}{dx^2}+(\gamma-x)\frac{dy}{dx}-\alpha y=0.\qquad(11.2)$$

From the definition of $(\beta)_r$, we see that

$$\lim_{\beta\to\infty}\frac{(\beta)_r}{\beta^r}=1$$

so that the function (11.1) is the series

$$\sum_{r=0}^{\infty} \frac{(\alpha)_r}{(\gamma)_r} \cdot \frac{x^r}{r!} \qquad (11.3)$$

and this series we denote by the symbol $_1F_1(\alpha; \gamma; x)$. This function is called a **confluent hypergeometric function,** and the equation (11.2) is the **confluent hypergeometric equation.**

Equations of the type (11.2) occur in mathematical physics in the discussion of boundary value problems in potential theory, and in the theory of atomic collisions (see examples 13, 14 below).

It is readily verified that the point $x = 0$ is a regular point of the differential equation (11.2) and that, in the notation of § 3, $p_0 = \gamma$ and $q_0 = 0$. The indicial equation is therefore

$$\varrho(\varrho + \gamma - 1) = 0$$

with roots $\varrho = 0$ and $\varrho = 1 - \gamma$.

Corresponding to the root $\varrho = 0$ there is a solution of the form

$$y_1 = \sum_{r=0}^{\infty} c_r x^r;$$

substituting this solution in equation (11.2) and equating to zero the coefficient of x^r we find that

$$c_{r+1} = \frac{(\alpha + r)c_r}{(\gamma + r)(r + 1)}.$$

Putting $c_0 = 1$ we see that

$$c_r = \frac{(\alpha)_r}{(\gamma)_r} \cdot \frac{1}{r!},$$

and if γ is neither zero nor a negative integer the solution is

$$y_1(x) = {}_1F_1(\alpha; \gamma; x). \qquad (11.4)$$

Similarly, the root $\varrho = 1 - \gamma$, leads, if $1 - \gamma$ is neither zero nor a positive integer, to a solution of the type

$$y_2(x) = x^{1-\gamma} \sum_{r=0}^{\infty} c_r x^r.$$

If we write

$$y_2(x) = x^{1-\gamma} u(x),$$

and substitute in (11.2) we find that $u(x)$ satisfies the equation

$$x \frac{d^2u}{dx^2} + (2-\gamma-x) \frac{du}{dx} - (\alpha-\gamma+1)u = 0,$$

which is the same as equation (11.2) with γ replaced by $2-\gamma$ and α replaced by $\alpha-\gamma+1$. We know from equation (11.4) that the solution of this equation which has value unity when $x = 0$ is $u = {}_1F_1(\alpha-\gamma+1;\ 2-\gamma;\ x)$ so that

$$y_2(x) = x^{1-\gamma} {}_1F_1(\alpha-\gamma+1;\ 2-\gamma;\ x). \tag{11.5}$$

Thus if γ is neither 0 nor an integer the general solution of equation (11.2) is

$$y(x) = A\,{}_1F_1(\alpha;\ \gamma;\ x) + Bx^{1-\gamma}\,{}_1F_1(\alpha-\gamma+1;\ 2-\gamma;\ x), \tag{11.6}$$

where A and B are arbitrary constants.

In the exceptional case $\gamma = 1$ we have

$$y_1(x) = {}_1F_1(\alpha;\ 1;\ x), \tag{11.7}$$

obtained simply by putting $\gamma = 1$ in equation (11.4). For the second solution we write

$$y_2(x) = y_1(x) \log x + \sum_{r=1}^{\infty} c_r x^r. \tag{11.8}$$

Substituting this expression in equation (11.2) we find that the unknown coefficients c_r must be such that

$$\frac{dy_1}{dx} - y_1 + \sum_{r=1}^{\infty} \{(r+1)^2 c_{r+1} - rc_r\}x^r + c_1 = 0.$$

Inserting the value of $y_1(x)$ from equation (11.7) we see

that these coefficients are determined by the recurrence relation

$$c_1 = 1-\alpha, \quad (r+1)^2 c_{r+1} - r c_r = (1-\alpha) \frac{(\alpha)_r}{r!(r+1)!}. \qquad (11.9)$$

The complete solution is therefore given by $y = A y_1(x) + B y_2(x)$ where A and B are arbitrary constants and the functions $y_1(x)$, $y_2(x)$ are defined by equations (11.7), (11.8) and (11.9). The complete solution when γ is an integer may be found by a similar method.

If in equation (11.2) we put

$$y(x) = x^{-\frac{1}{2}\gamma} e^{\frac{1}{2}x} W(x) \qquad (11.10)$$

we find that the function $W(x)$ satisfies the differential equation

$$\frac{d^2 W}{dx^2} + \left\{ -\tfrac{1}{4} + \frac{k}{x} + \frac{\tfrac{1}{4} - m^2}{x^2} \right\} W(x) = 0, \qquad (11.11)$$

where we have written k for $\tfrac{1}{2}\gamma - \alpha$ and m for $(\tfrac{1}{2} - \tfrac{1}{2}\gamma)$. The solutions of this equation are known as **Whittaker's confluent hypergeometric functions.**

If $2m$ is neither 1 nor an integer the solutions of the confluent hypergeometric equation corresponding to equation (11.11) are given by equation (11.6) with $\gamma = 1 + 2m$ and $\alpha = \tfrac{1}{2} - k + m$. Thus the solutions of equation (11.11) are the Whittaker functions

$$M_{k,\,m}(x) = x^{\frac{1}{2}+m} e^{-\frac{1}{2}x} {}_1F_1(\tfrac{1}{2}-k+m; \, 1+2m; \, x), \qquad (11.12a)$$

$$M_{k,\,-m}(x) = x^{\frac{1}{2}-m} e^{-\frac{1}{2}x} {}_1F_1(\tfrac{1}{2}-k-m; \, 1-2m; \, x). \qquad (11.12b)$$

Several of the properties of ${}_2F_1$ functions have analogues for the ${}_1F_1$ functions. Corresponding to equation (7.1) there is the integral formula

$$_1F_1(\alpha; \, \gamma; \, x) = \frac{1}{B(\alpha, \, \gamma-\alpha)} \int_0^1 (1-t)^{\gamma-\alpha-1} t^{\alpha-1} e^{xt} dt, \qquad (11.13)$$

from which Kummer's relation

$$_1F_1(\alpha; \gamma; x) = e^x \, _1F_1(\gamma - \alpha; \gamma; -x) \qquad (11.14)$$

may be obtained by a simple change of variable. The analogue of equation (6.5) is

$$\frac{d}{dx}\{_1F_1(\alpha; \gamma; x)\} = \frac{a}{\gamma} \, _1F_1(\alpha + 1; \gamma + 1; x), \qquad (11.15)$$

while corresponding to the contiguity relations of § 10 we have relations of the type

$$\alpha \, _1F_1(\alpha + 1; \gamma + 1; x) + (\gamma - \alpha) \, _1F_1(\alpha; \gamma + 1; x)$$
$$- \gamma \, _1F_1(\alpha; \gamma; x) = 0, \qquad (11.16)$$

$$(x + \alpha) \, _1F_1(\alpha + 1; \gamma + 1; x) + (\gamma - \alpha) \, _1F_1(\alpha; \gamma + 1; x)$$
$$- \gamma \, _1F_1(\alpha + 1; \gamma; x) = 0, \qquad (11.17)$$

$$\alpha \, _1F_1(\alpha + 1; \gamma; x) + (\gamma - 2\alpha - x) \, _1F_1(\alpha; \gamma; x)$$
$$+ (\alpha - \gamma) \, _1F_1(\alpha - 1; \gamma; x) = 0, \qquad (11.18)$$

$$(\alpha - \gamma)x \, _1F_1(\alpha; \gamma + 1; x) + \gamma(x + \gamma - 1) \, _1F_1(\alpha; \gamma; x)$$
$$+ \gamma(\gamma - 1) \, _1F_1(\alpha; \gamma - 1; x) = 0. \qquad (11.19)$$

§ 12. **Generalised hypergeometric series.** There are two ways by which we may approach the problem of generalising the idea of a hypergeometric function. We may think of such a function as being the solution of a linear differential equation which is an immediate generalisation of the equation (8.1) or we can define the function by a series which is analogous to the series (6.1).

At first sight it is difficult to see how the differential equation (8.1) can be generalised immediately, but if we introduce the operator

$$\vartheta = x \frac{d}{dx}$$

and notice that (8.1) is equivalent to

$$\{\vartheta(\vartheta+\gamma-1)-x(\vartheta+\alpha)(\vartheta+\beta)\}y = 0, \qquad (12.1)$$

an obvious generalisation is

$$\{\vartheta(\vartheta+\varrho_1-1)...(\vartheta+\varrho_p-1)-x(\vartheta+\alpha_1)...(\vartheta+\alpha_{p+1})\}y = 0, \qquad (12.2)$$

where α_1, α_2, ..., α_{p+1}, ϱ_1, ..., ϱ_p are constants. Furthermore it is readily shown that this equation is satisfied by the series

$$\sum_{n=0}^{\infty} \frac{(\alpha_1)_n(\alpha_2)_n...(\alpha_{p+1})_n}{(\varrho_1)_n(\varrho_2)_n...(\varrho_p)_n} \cdot \frac{x^n}{n!}, \qquad (12.3)$$

which is, itself, a generalisation of the series (6.1). Such a series is called a **generalised hypergeometric series** and is denoted by the symbol $_{p+1}F_p(\alpha_1, ..., \alpha_{p+1}; \varrho_1, ..., \varrho_p; x)$. It is left as an exercise to the reader to show that, if no two of the numbers 1, ϱ_1, ϱ_2, ..., ϱ_p differ by an integer (or zero), the other p linearly independent solutions of equation (12.2) are

$$x^{1-\varrho_i}{}_{p+1}F_p(1+\alpha_1-\varrho_i..., 1+\alpha_{p+1}-\varrho_i; 2-\varrho_i,$$
$$1+\varrho_1-\varrho_2, ..., 1+\varrho_p-\varrho_i; x), \quad (i = 1, 2, ..., n).$$

As it stands (12.3) is a generalisation of the series (6.1) but it is not sufficiently wide to cover a simple series of the type (11.3). To cover such cases we generalise, not the differential equation, but the series defining the function. The generalisation of (6.1) which includes (12.3) is the series

$$\sum_{n=0}^{\infty} \frac{(\alpha_1)_n(\alpha_2)_n...(\alpha_p)_n}{(\varrho_1)_n(\varrho_2)_n...(\varrho_q)_n} \cdot \frac{x^n}{n!}, \qquad (12.4)$$

which we denote by the symbol

$$_pF_q(\alpha_1, ...\alpha_p; \varrho_1, ...\varrho_q; x),$$

or, if we wish particularly to throw into relief the difference between the numerator and the denominator parameters, by the symbol

$$_pF_q\left[\begin{matrix} \alpha_1, \ldots, \alpha_p; \; x \\ \varrho_1, \ldots, \varrho_q; \end{matrix}\right].$$

The suffix p in front of the F denotes that there are p numerator parameters $\alpha_1, \ldots, \alpha_p$; similarly the suffix q indicates the number of denominator parameters.

Generalised hypergeometric series do not usually arise in mathematical physics because we have to solve equations of the type (12.2). Their use is more indirect. Such series occur normally only in the evaluation of integrals involving special functions. In certain cases these series reduce to series of the type

$$_pF_q\left[\begin{matrix} \alpha_1, \ldots, \alpha_p; \; 1 \\ \varrho_1, \ldots, \varrho_q; \end{matrix}\right]$$

which have unit argument. For this reason it is desirable to have information about sums of this type. An account of the theory of such sums is given in W. N. Bailey, *Generalised Hypergeometric Series* (Cambridge University Press, 1935). Here we shall consider only one such calculation because it illustrates the use of the theorems of Gauss and Kummer proved above (equations (7.2) and (7.3) respectively). Other results of this kind are given in examples 18 and 20 below.

By expanding the $_3F_2$ series involved we see that

$$S \equiv \frac{\Gamma(\alpha)\Gamma(\beta)\Gamma(\gamma)}{\Gamma(1+\alpha-\beta)\Gamma(1+\alpha-\gamma)} \, _3F_2\left[\begin{matrix} \alpha, & \beta, & \gamma; & 1 \\ 1+\alpha-\beta, & 1+\alpha-\gamma; & \end{matrix}\right]$$

$$= \sum_{n=0}^{\infty} \frac{\Gamma(\alpha+n)\Gamma(\beta+n)\Gamma(\gamma+n)}{n!\,\Gamma(1+\alpha-\beta+n)\Gamma(1+\alpha-\gamma+n)}$$

$$= \sum_{n=0}^{\infty} \frac{\Gamma(\alpha+n)\Gamma(\beta+n)\Gamma(\gamma+n)}{n!\,\Gamma(1+\alpha+2n)\Gamma(1+\alpha-\beta-\gamma)}$$

$$\left\{\frac{\Gamma(1+\alpha+2n)\Gamma(1+\alpha-\beta-\gamma)}{\Gamma(1+\alpha-\beta+n)\Gamma(1+\alpha-\gamma+n)}\right\}.$$

Now by Gauss's theorem (7.2) the expression inside the curly brackets is equal to $_2F_1(\beta+n, \gamma+n; 1+\alpha+2n; 1)$ which may be written

$$\sum_{m=0}^{\infty} \frac{\Gamma(\beta+n+m)\Gamma(\gamma+n+m)\Gamma(1+\alpha+2n)}{\Gamma(\beta+n)\Gamma(\gamma+n)\Gamma(1+\alpha+2n+m)m!};$$

whence we find that

$$S = \sum_{n=0}^{\infty}\sum_{m=0}^{\infty} \frac{\Gamma(\alpha+n)\Gamma(\beta+n+m)\Gamma(\gamma+n+m)}{\Gamma(1+\alpha+2n+m)\Gamma(1+\alpha-\beta-\gamma)n!m!}.$$

Interchanging the order of summation and putting $p = n+m$ we see that

$$S = \sum_{p=0}^{\infty} \frac{\Gamma(\beta+p)\Gamma(\gamma+p)}{\Gamma(1+\alpha-\beta-\gamma)} \sum_{n=0}^{p} \frac{\Gamma(\alpha+n)}{n!(p-n)!\Gamma(1+\alpha+n+p)}.$$

Now by example 9 (iii) of Chapter I

$$\frac{1}{(p-n)!} = (-1)^n \frac{(-p)_n}{p!},$$

so that the inner sum is equal to

$$\frac{\Gamma(\alpha)}{p!\Gamma(1+\alpha+p)} {}_2F_1\left[\begin{array}{c} \alpha, -p; -1 \\ 1+\alpha+p \end{array}\right],$$

which by Kummer's theorem (7.3) is equal to

$$\frac{\Gamma(\alpha)\Gamma(1+\tfrac{1}{2}\alpha)}{p!\Gamma(1+\alpha)\Gamma(1+\tfrac{1}{2}\alpha+p)}.$$

Therefore

$$S = \sum_{p=0} \frac{\Gamma(\alpha)\Gamma(\beta+p)\Gamma(\gamma+p)\Gamma(1+\tfrac{1}{2}\alpha)}{p!(1+\alpha-\beta-\gamma)\Gamma(1+\alpha)\Gamma(1+\tfrac{1}{2}\alpha+p)}$$

$$= \frac{\Gamma(\alpha)\Gamma(\beta)\Gamma(\gamma)}{\Gamma(1+\alpha)\Gamma(1+\alpha-\beta-\gamma)} {}_2F_1\left[\begin{array}{c} \beta, \gamma; 1 \\ 1+\tfrac{1}{2}\alpha; \end{array}\right].$$

D

This $_2F_1$ series with unit argument can be summed by Gauss's formula (7.2) and the expression for S found. It then follows that

$$_3F_2\begin{bmatrix} \alpha, & \beta, & \gamma; & 1 \\ 1+\alpha-\beta, & 1+\alpha-\gamma; & \end{bmatrix}$$

$$= \frac{\Gamma(1+\tfrac{1}{2}\alpha)\Gamma(1+\tfrac{1}{2}\alpha-\beta-\gamma)\Gamma(1+\alpha-\beta)\Gamma(1+\alpha-\gamma)}{\Gamma(1+\alpha)\Gamma(1+\alpha-\beta-\gamma)\Gamma(1+\tfrac{1}{2}\alpha-\beta)\Gamma(1+\tfrac{1}{2}\alpha-\gamma)},$$

a result which is known as **Dixon's theorem**.

Examples II

(1) Show that

(i) $_2F_1(\alpha, \beta; \beta; z) = (1-z)^{-\alpha}$;

(ii) $_2F_1(\tfrac{1}{2}\alpha, \tfrac{1}{2}\alpha+\tfrac{1}{2}; \tfrac{1}{2}; z) = \tfrac{1}{2}\{(1-z)^{-\alpha}+(1+z)^{-\alpha}\}$;

(iii) $_2F_1(\tfrac{1}{2}\alpha+\tfrac{1}{2}, \tfrac{1}{2}\alpha+1; \tfrac{3}{2}; z^2) = \dfrac{1}{2\alpha z}\{(1-z)^{-\alpha}-(1+z)^{-\alpha}\}$;

(iv) $_2F_1(1, 1; 2; z) = -\dfrac{1}{z}\log(1-z)$;

(v) $_2F_1(\tfrac{1}{2}, 1; \tfrac{3}{2}; z^2) = \dfrac{1}{2z}\log\dfrac{1+z}{1-z}$;

(vi) $_2F_1(\tfrac{1}{2}, \tfrac{1}{2}; \tfrac{3}{2}; z^2) = \dfrac{\sin^{-1}z}{z}$;

(vii) $_2F_1(\tfrac{1}{2}, 1; \tfrac{3}{2}; -z^2) = \dfrac{\tan^{-1}z}{z}$;

(viii) $_2F_1(\tfrac{1}{2}, \tfrac{1}{2}; 1; k^2) = \dfrac{2}{\pi}K(k)$;

(ix) $_2F_1(-\tfrac{1}{2}, \tfrac{1}{2}; 1; k^2) = \dfrac{2}{\pi}E(k)$.

(2) By transforming the equation $y'' + n^2 y = 0$ to hypergeometric form by the substitution $\xi = \sin^2 z$, prove that, if $-\frac{1}{2}\pi \leq z \leq \frac{1}{2}\pi$,

(i) $\cos(nz) = {}_2F_1(\frac{1}{2}n, -\frac{1}{2}n; \frac{1}{2}; \sin^2 z)$;

(ii) $\sin(nz) = n \sin z \, {}_2F_1(\frac{1}{2} - \frac{1}{2}n, \frac{1}{2} + \frac{1}{2}n; \frac{3}{2}; \sin^2 z)$;

and that, if $0 \leq z \leq \pi$,

(iii) $\cos(nz) = \cos(\frac{1}{2}n\pi) \, {}_2F_1(\frac{1}{2}n, -\frac{1}{2}n; \frac{1}{2}; \cos^2 z)$
$+ n \sin(\frac{1}{2}n\pi) \cos(z) \, {}_2F_1(\frac{1}{2} - \frac{1}{2}n, \frac{1}{2} + \frac{1}{2}n; \frac{3}{2}; \cos^2 z)$;

(iv) $\sin(nz) = \sin(\frac{1}{2}n\pi) \, {}_2F_1(\frac{1}{2}n, -\frac{1}{2}n; \frac{1}{2}; \cos^2 z)$
$- n \cos(\frac{1}{2}n\pi) \cos(z) \, {}_2F_1(\frac{1}{2} - \frac{1}{2}n, \frac{1}{2} + \frac{1}{2}n; \frac{3}{2}; \cos^2 z)$;

(3) Prove the relations:

(i) $(\alpha - \beta)(1 - x) \, {}_2F_1(\alpha, \beta; \gamma; x)$
$= (\gamma - \beta) {}_2F_1(\alpha, \beta - 1; \gamma; x) - (\gamma - \alpha) {}_2F(\alpha - 1, \beta; \gamma; x)$;

(ii) $(\gamma - \beta - 1) {}_2F_1(\alpha, \beta; \gamma; x)$
$= (\gamma - \alpha - \beta - 1) {}_2F_1(\alpha, \beta + 1; \gamma; x) + \alpha(1 - x) {}_2F_1(\alpha + 1, \beta + 1; \gamma; x)$;
$= (\alpha - \beta - 1)(1 - x) {}_2F_1(\alpha, \beta + 1; \gamma; x) + (\gamma - \alpha) {}_2F_1(\alpha - 1, \beta + 1; \gamma; x)$;

(iii) $(\gamma - \alpha - \beta) {}_2F_1(\alpha, \beta; \gamma; x)$
$= (\gamma - \alpha) {}_2F_1(\alpha - 1, \beta; \gamma; x) - \beta(1 - x) {}_2F_1(\alpha, \beta + 1; \gamma; x)$;

(iv) $\alpha {}_2F_1(\alpha + 1; \beta; \gamma; x) - (\gamma - 1) {}_2F_1(\alpha, \beta; \gamma - 1; x)$
$= (\alpha + 1 - \gamma) {}_2F_1(\alpha, \beta; \gamma; x)$;

(v) $(1 - x) \, {}_2F_1(\alpha, \beta; \gamma; x) - {}_2F_1(\alpha - 1, \beta - 1; \gamma; x)$

$$= \frac{\alpha + \beta - \gamma - 1}{\gamma} x \, {}_2F_1(\alpha, \beta; \gamma + 1; x)$$;

(vi) $\dfrac{(1 - \beta)x}{\gamma} \, {}_2F_1(\alpha, \beta; \gamma + 1; x)$

$= {}_2F_1(\alpha - 1, \beta - 1; \gamma; x) - {}_2F_1(\alpha, \beta - 1; \gamma; x)$;

(vii) $(1-x)\,_2F_1(\alpha,\,\beta;\,\gamma;\,x)$

$$= \,_2F_1(\alpha,\,\beta-1;\,\gamma;\,x) + \frac{(\alpha-\gamma)x}{\gamma}\,_2F_1(\alpha,\,\beta;\,\gamma+1;\,x).$$

4. Prove that

(i) $\,_2F_1(\alpha,\,\beta+1;\,\gamma+1;\,z) - \,_2F_1(\alpha,\,\beta;\,\gamma;\,z)$

$$= \frac{\alpha(\gamma-\beta)}{\gamma(\gamma+1)}\,z\,_2F_1(\alpha+1,\,\beta+1;\,\gamma+2;\,z);$$

(ii) $\,_2F_1(\alpha,\,\beta;\,\gamma;\,z) = \,_2F_1(\alpha+1,\,\beta-1;\,\gamma;\,z)$

$$+ \frac{\alpha-\beta+1}{\gamma}\,z\,_2F_1(\alpha+1,\,\beta;\,\gamma+1;\,z).$$

Deduce a simple expression for the hypergeometric series $\,_2F_1(\alpha,\,\beta;\,\beta-1;\,z)$.

(5) If n is a positive integer, prove that

$\,_2F_1(-n,\,\alpha+n;\,\gamma;\,x)$

$$= \frac{x^{1-\gamma}(1-x)^{\gamma-\alpha}\Gamma(\gamma)}{\Gamma(\gamma+n)}\frac{d^n}{dx^n}\{x^{\gamma+n-1}(1-x)^{\alpha-\gamma+n}\},$$

and deduce that

$$_2F_1\left(-n,\,\alpha+n;\,\tfrac{1}{2}\alpha+\tfrac{1}{2};\,\frac{1-\mu}{2}\right)$$

$$= \frac{(\mu^2-1)^{\frac{1}{2}-\frac{1}{2}\alpha}\Gamma(\tfrac{1}{2}\alpha+\tfrac{1}{2})}{2^n\Gamma(\tfrac{1}{2}\alpha+\tfrac{1}{2}+n)}\frac{d^n}{d\mu^n}(\mu^2-1)^{n+\frac{1}{2}\alpha-\frac{1}{2}}.$$

(6) If n is a positive integer, and $|x|>1$, prove that

$$_2F_1\left(\frac{n+1}{2},\,\frac{n+2}{2};\,1;\,-\frac{1}{x^2}\right) = \frac{(-1)^n x^{n+1}}{n!}\frac{d^n}{dx^n}\left\{\frac{1}{\sqrt{(x^2+1)}}\right\}.$$

(7) Establish the following formulæ:

(i) $\,_2F_1(\alpha;\,\beta;\,\alpha+\beta+\varrho;\,x)\times\,_2F_1(\gamma;\,\delta;\,\gamma+\delta-\varrho;\,x)$

$= \,_2F_1(\alpha+\varrho,\beta+\varrho;\,\alpha+\beta+\varrho;\,x)\times\,_2F_1(\gamma-\varrho,\delta-\varrho;\,\gamma+\delta-\varrho;\,x);$

(ii) $D_x\{x^\alpha \, {}_2F_1(\alpha, \beta; \gamma; kx)\} = \alpha x^{\alpha-1} \, {}_2F_1(\alpha+1; \beta; \gamma; kx)$,
where $\alpha \neq 0$;

(iii) $B(\lambda, \gamma-\lambda) \, {}_2F_1(\alpha, \beta; \gamma; x)$

$$= \int_0^1 t^{\lambda-1}(1-t)^{\gamma-\lambda-1} \, {}_2F_1(\alpha, \beta; \lambda; xt)dt,$$

where $|x| < 1$, $\lambda > 0$, $\gamma - \lambda > 0$.

(8) Prove that if $\beta > 0$,

$${}_2F_1(\alpha, \beta; 2\beta; z)$$

$$= \frac{(1-\frac{1}{2}z)^{-\alpha}}{2^{2\beta-1}B(\beta, \beta)} \int_0^{\frac{1}{2}\pi} (\sin \phi)^{2\beta-1} \left[\begin{matrix} \{1+\zeta \cos \phi\}^{-\alpha} \\ +\{1-\zeta \cos \phi\}^{-\alpha} \end{matrix} \right] d\phi,$$

where $\zeta = z/(2-z)$.
Deduce that

$${}_2F_1(\alpha, \beta; 2\beta; z) = (1-\tfrac{1}{2}z)^{-\alpha} \, {}_2F_1(\tfrac{1}{2}\alpha, \tfrac{1}{2}\alpha+\tfrac{1}{2}; \beta+\tfrac{1}{2}; \zeta^2).$$

(9) Prove that

$$\int_0^{\frac{1}{2}\pi} \cos m\theta \cos^n \theta \, d\theta = \frac{\pi\Gamma(n+1)}{2^{n+1}\Gamma(\frac{1}{2}n+\frac{1}{2}m+1)\Gamma(\frac{1}{2}n-\frac{1}{2}m+1)}$$

and evaluate

$$\int_0^{\frac{1}{2}\pi} \cos 2m\theta \sin^n \theta \, d\theta$$

where m is a positive integer.

(10) Schrödinger's equation for the rotation of a symmetrical-top molecule is

$$\frac{1}{\sin \theta} \frac{\partial}{\partial \theta} \left(\sin \theta \frac{\partial \psi}{\partial \theta} \right) + \frac{1}{\sin^2 \theta} \frac{\partial^2 \psi}{\partial \phi^2}$$

$$+ \left(\cot^2 \theta + \frac{A}{C} \right) \frac{\partial^2 \psi}{\partial \chi^2} - \frac{2\cos \theta}{\sin^2 \theta} \frac{\partial^2 \psi}{\partial \chi \partial \phi} + \frac{8\pi^2 A W}{h^2} \psi = 0,$$

where A, C, W, h are constants. Show that it possesses solutions of the form

$$\psi = e^{im\phi - in\chi}(1-x)^{\frac{1}{2}(n-m)} x^{\frac{1}{2}(n-m)} {}_2F_1(\alpha, \beta; \gamma; x),$$

where $n \geq m$, $x = \frac{1}{2}(1 - \cos\theta)$, $\gamma = n - m + 1$, and α, β are the roots of the equation

$$z^2 - (2n+1)z + \frac{A}{C}n^2 + n - \frac{8\pi^2 AW}{h^2} = 0.$$

(11) Prove that:

(i) ${}_1F_1(\alpha; \alpha; x) = e^x$;

(ii) ${}_1F_1(\alpha+1; \alpha; x) = \left(1 + \frac{x}{\alpha}\right)e^x$;

(iii) ${}_1F_1(\frac{1}{2}; \frac{3}{2}; -x^2) = \frac{\sqrt{\pi}}{2x}\,\mathrm{erf}\,(x)$;

(iv) ${}_1F_1(\alpha+1; \gamma; x) - {}_1F_1(\alpha; \gamma; x) = \frac{x}{\gamma}{}_1F_1(\alpha+1; \gamma+1; x)$;

(v) ${}_1F_1(-\frac{1}{2}; \frac{1}{2}; -x^2) = e^{-x^2} - \sqrt{\pi}\,x\,\mathrm{erf}\,(x)$;

(vi) $x^n\,{}_1F_1(n; n+1; -x) = n\displaystyle\int_0^x t^{n-1}e^{-t}\,dt$.

(12) Prove that the equation

$$\frac{\partial^2 V}{\partial x^2} = \frac{1}{k}\frac{\partial V}{\partial t}$$

possesses solutions of the type

$$V = Ct^m\,{}_1F_1\left(-m; \frac{1}{2}; -\frac{x^2}{4kt}\right)$$

where m and C are constants.

(13) Show that the Schrödinger equation

$$\nabla^2\psi + \left(k^2 - \frac{\beta}{r}\right)\psi = 0$$

possesses a solution of the form

$$e^{ikz} {}_1F_1\left(-\frac{i\beta}{2k}; 1; ikr - ikz\right).$$

(14) The Schrödinger equation governing the radial wave functions for positive energy states in a Coulomb field is

$$\frac{1}{r}\frac{d}{dr}\left(r\frac{dL}{dr}\right) + \left[\frac{8\pi^2 m}{h^2}\left(W - \frac{zz'e^2}{r}\right) - \frac{n(n+1)}{r^2}\right]L = 0.$$

Show that it possesses a solution

$$L = r^n e^{ikr} {}_1F_1(i\alpha + n + 1; 2n + 2; -2ikr)$$

where $k^2 = 8\pi^2 mW/h^2$, $\alpha = 4\pi^2 mzz'e^2/k$.

(15) Show that the equation

$$\frac{d^2y}{dx^2} + \frac{1}{x}\frac{dy}{dx} + \left\{m^2 - \frac{2m\beta}{x} - \frac{n^2}{x^2}\right\}y = 0$$

possesses a solution

$$y = x^{\frac{1}{2}n} e^{-\frac{1}{2}x} {}_1F_1(\tfrac{1}{2}n + \tfrac{1}{2} - i\beta; 2imx)$$

and hence that a solution of equation (1.9c) is

$$R = \varrho^{\frac{1}{2}n} e^{-\frac{1}{2}\varrho} F(\tfrac{1}{2}n + \tfrac{1}{2}; n + 1; 2im\varrho).$$

(16) Show that

(i) $$\int_0^1 x^{l-1}(1-x)^{m-1} {}_pF_q\begin{bmatrix}\alpha_1, \dots, \alpha_p, \kappa x\\ \beta_1, \dots, \beta_q;\end{bmatrix}dx$$

$$= B(1, m) {}_{p+1}F_{q+1}\begin{bmatrix}\alpha_1, \dots, \alpha_p, l; \kappa\\ \beta_1, \dots, \beta_q, l+m;\end{bmatrix};$$

(ii) $\displaystyle\int_0^1 x^{l-1}(1-x)^{m-1} \, {}_pF_q\left[\begin{array}{c} \alpha_1, ..., \alpha_p; \; \dfrac{1-x}{2} \\ \beta_1, ..., \beta_q; \end{array}\right] dx$

$$= B(1, m)_{p+1}F_{+q1}\left[\begin{array}{c} \alpha_1, ..., \alpha_p, m; \; \frac{1}{2} \\ \beta_1, ..., \beta_q, l+m \end{array}\right];$$

(iii) $\displaystyle\int^1 (1-x^2)^{m-1} \, {}_pF_q\left[\begin{array}{c} \alpha_1, ..., \alpha_p; \; \dfrac{1-x}{2} \\ \beta_1, ..., \beta_q \end{array}\right] dx$

$$= B(\tfrac{1}{2}, m)_{p+1}F_{q+1}\left[\begin{array}{c} \alpha_1, ..., \alpha_p, m; \; 1 \\ \beta_1, ..., \beta_q, 2m; \end{array}\right].$$

(17) Prove that

(i) $\displaystyle\int_0^\infty {}_pF_q\left[\begin{array}{c} \alpha_1, ..., \alpha_p; \; bx \\ \beta_1, ..., \beta_q; \end{array}\right] e^{-ax} x^{\mu-1} \, dx$

$$= \frac{\Gamma(\mu)}{a^\mu} {}_{p+1}F_q\left[\begin{array}{c} \alpha_1, ..., \alpha_p, \mu; \; b/a \\ \beta_1, ..., \beta_q; \end{array}\right];$$

(ii) $\displaystyle\int_0^\infty {}_pF_q\left[\begin{array}{c} \alpha_1, ..., \alpha_p; \; \pm b^2 x^2 \\ \beta_1, ..., \beta_q; \end{array}\right] e^{-ax} x^{\mu-1} \, dx$

$$= \frac{\Gamma(\mu)}{a^\mu} {}_{p+2}F_q\left[\begin{array}{c} \alpha_1. ..., \alpha_p, \tfrac{1}{2}\mu, \tfrac{1}{2}\mu+\tfrac{1}{2}; \; \pm 4b^2/a^2 \\ \beta_1 .., \beta_q; \end{array}\right];$$

(iii) $\displaystyle\int_0^\infty {}_pF_q\left[\begin{array}{c} \alpha_1, ..., \alpha_p; \; \pm b^2 x^2 \\ \beta_1, ..., \beta_q; \end{array}\right] e^{-p^2 x^2} x^{\mu-1} \, dx$

$$= \frac{\Gamma(\tfrac{1}{2}\mu)}{2p^\mu} {}_{p+1}F_q\left[\begin{array}{c} \alpha_1, ..., \alpha_p, \tfrac{1}{2}\mu; \; \pm b^2/p^2 \\ \beta_1, ..., \beta_q; \end{array}\right].$$

(18) By equating coefficients of x in the relation

$$(1-x)^{\alpha-\beta-\gamma} {}_2F_1(\alpha, \beta; \gamma; x) = {}_2F_1(\gamma-\alpha, \gamma-\beta; \gamma; x)$$

prove **Saalschutz's theorem**

$$
{}_3F_2 \begin{bmatrix} \alpha, \beta, -n; 1 \\ \gamma, 1+\alpha+\beta-\gamma-n \end{bmatrix} = \frac{(\gamma-\alpha)_n(\gamma-\beta)_n}{(\gamma)_n(\gamma-\alpha-\beta)_n}.
$$

Hence prove that

$$
{}_2F_1 \begin{bmatrix} \alpha, \beta; x \\ 1+\alpha-\beta \end{bmatrix} = (1-x)^{-\alpha} \, {}_2F_1 \begin{bmatrix} \tfrac{1}{2}\alpha, \tfrac{1}{2}+\tfrac{1}{2}\alpha-\beta; \; -\dfrac{4x}{(1-x)^2} \\ 1+\alpha-\beta; \end{bmatrix}
$$

if $|x| < 3 - 2\sqrt{2}$.

(19) Show that

$$
{}_2F_1(\alpha, \beta; 1+\alpha-\beta; z)
$$
$$
= (1-z)^{-\alpha} \, {}_2F_1(\tfrac{1}{2}\alpha, \tfrac{1}{2}+\tfrac{1}{2}\alpha-\beta; 1+\alpha-\beta; \zeta)
$$

where $\zeta = -4z(1-z)^{-2}$. Hence deduce the value of ${}_2F_1(\alpha, \beta; 1+\alpha-\beta; -1)$ from Gauss's theorem.

(20) Show that

$$
{}_3F_2 \begin{bmatrix} \alpha, \beta, \gamma; 1 \\ \delta, \varepsilon; \end{bmatrix}
$$
$$
= \frac{\Gamma(\delta)\Gamma(\varepsilon)\Gamma(\sigma)}{\Gamma(\alpha)\Gamma(\sigma+\beta)\Gamma(\sigma+\gamma)} \, {}_3F_2 \begin{bmatrix} \delta-\alpha, \varepsilon-\alpha, \sigma; 1 \\ \sigma+\beta, \sigma+\gamma \end{bmatrix}
$$

where $\sigma = \delta+\varepsilon-\alpha-\beta-\gamma$.

Hence, using Dixon's theorem, prove **Watson's theorem**:

$$
{}_3F_2 \begin{bmatrix} \alpha, \beta, \gamma; 1 \\ \tfrac{1}{2}(1+\alpha+\beta), 2\gamma; \end{bmatrix}
$$
$$
= \frac{\Gamma(\tfrac{1}{2})\Gamma(\tfrac{1}{2}+\gamma)\Gamma(\tfrac{1}{2}+\tfrac{1}{2}\alpha+\tfrac{1}{2}\beta)\Gamma(\tfrac{1}{2}-\tfrac{1}{2}\alpha-\tfrac{1}{2}\beta+\gamma)}{\Gamma(\tfrac{1}{2}+\tfrac{1}{2}\alpha)\Gamma(\tfrac{1}{2}+\tfrac{1}{2}\beta)\Gamma(\tfrac{1}{2}-\tfrac{1}{2}\alpha+\gamma)\Gamma(\tfrac{1}{2}-\tfrac{1}{2}\beta+\gamma)}
$$

and, using Watson's theorem, deduce **Whipple's theorem** that, if $\alpha+\beta = 1$, and $\varepsilon+\delta = 2\gamma+1$,

$$
{}_3F_2 \begin{bmatrix} \alpha, \beta, \gamma; 1 \\ \delta, \varepsilon; \end{bmatrix}
$$
$$
= \frac{\pi\Gamma(\delta)\Gamma(\varepsilon)}{2^{2\gamma-1}\Gamma(\tfrac{1}{2}\alpha+\tfrac{1}{2}\delta)\Gamma(\tfrac{1}{2}\alpha+\tfrac{1}{2}\varepsilon)\Gamma(\tfrac{1}{2}\beta+\tfrac{1}{2}\delta)\Gamma(\tfrac{1}{2}\beta+\tfrac{1}{2}\varepsilon)}.
$$

CHAPTER III

LEGENDRE FUNCTIONS

§ 13. Legendre polynomials. If A is a fixed point with coordinates (α, β, γ) and P is the variable point (x, y, z), then if we denote the distance AP by R, we have

$$R^2 = (x-\alpha)^2 + (y-\beta)^2 + (z-\gamma)^2.$$

Furthermore, we know from elementary considerations that

$$\psi = \frac{1}{R}$$

is the gravitational potential at the point P due to a unit mass situated at the point A, and that this must be a particular solution of Laplace's equation.

In some circumstances it is desirable to expand ψ in powers of r or r^{-1} where $r = (x^2+y^2+z^2)^{\frac{1}{2}}$ is the distance of P from O, the origin of coordinates. This expansion can be obtained by the use of Taylor's theorem for functions of three variables but it is much more suitable to introduce the angle θ between the directions OA, OP (cf. fig. 4) and write

$$R^2 = r^2 + a^2 - 2ar \cos \theta.$$

The expression for ψ then becomes

$$\psi = \frac{1}{\sqrt{(a^2 - 2ar\mu + r^2)}} \tag{13.1}$$

where μ denotes $\cos \theta$, and this can be expanded in powers of r/a when $r<a$ and in powers of a/r when $r>a$. If we denote by $P_n(\mu)$ the coefficient of h^n in the expansion of $(1-2\mu h+h^2)^{-\frac{1}{2}}$ in ascending powers of h, i.e. if

$$\frac{1}{\sqrt{(1-2\mu h+h^2)}} = \sum_{n=0}^{\infty} P_n(\mu)h^n, \qquad (13.2)$$

then the potential function (13.1) can be expanded in

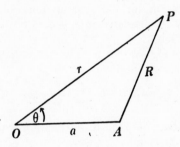

Fig. 4

the forms

$$\frac{1}{a} \sum_{n=0}^{\infty} \left(\frac{r}{a}\right)^n P_n(\mu), \qquad r<a; \qquad (13.3a)$$

$$\frac{1}{r} \sum_{n=0}^{\infty} \left(\frac{a}{r}\right)^n P_n(\mu), \qquad r>a. \qquad (13.3b)$$

It is clear from the definition (13.2) that the coefficients $P_n(\mu)$ are polynomials in μ. The first one or two can readily be calculated directly from the definition. By the binomial theorem we have

$$(1-2\mu h+h^2)^{-\frac{1}{2}}$$
$$= 1+(-\tfrac{1}{2})(-2\mu h+h^2)+ \frac{(-\tfrac{1}{2})(-\tfrac{3}{2})}{2}(-2\mu h+h^2)^2+\dots$$
$$= 1+\mu h+\tfrac{1}{2}(3\mu^2-1)h^2+\tfrac{1}{2}(5\mu^3-3\mu)h^3+\dots$$

so that

$$P_0(\mu) = 1, \quad P_1(\mu) = \mu,$$
$$P_2(\mu) = \tfrac{1}{2}(3\mu^2 - 1), \quad P_3(\mu) = \tfrac{1}{2}(5\mu^3 - 3\mu). \quad (13.4a)$$

We shall show below that, in the general case $P_n(\mu)$ is a polynomial in μ of degree n; it is called the **Legendre polynomial of order n**.

The expression for the general polynomial $P_n(\mu)$ can be derived by the method employed to obtain the simple expressions (13.4a).

Expanding $(1 - 2\mu h + h^2)^{-\frac{1}{2}}$ by the binomial theorem we have

$$(1 - 2\mu h + h^2)^{-\frac{1}{2}} = \sum_{r=0}^{\infty} \frac{(\tfrac{1}{2})_r}{r!} (2\mu h - h^2)^r$$

and the coefficient of h^n in this expansion is the coefficient of h^n in the expansion

$$\sum_{r=0}^{n} \frac{(\tfrac{1}{2})_r}{r!} (2\mu h - h^2)^r = \sum_{\varrho=0}^{n} \frac{(\tfrac{1}{2})_{n-\varrho}}{(n-\varrho)!} (2\mu h - h^2)^{n-\varrho}$$

$$= \sum_{\varrho=0}^{n} (-1)^{\varrho} \frac{(\tfrac{1}{2})_n}{(\tfrac{1}{2}-n)_{\varrho}} \frac{(2\mu h - h^2)^{n-\varrho}}{(n-\varrho)!},$$

since by example 9 (ii) of Chapter I

$$(-1)^{\varrho}(\tfrac{1}{2})_{n-\varrho} = \frac{(\tfrac{1}{2})_n}{(\tfrac{1}{2}-n)_{\varrho}}.$$

Now the coefficient of h^n in the expansion of

$$\frac{(-1)^{\varrho}}{(n-\varrho)!} (2\mu h - h^2)^{n-\varrho}$$

is

$$\frac{(2\mu)^{n-2\varrho}}{\varrho!(n-2\varrho)!},$$

and, by the duplication formula for the gamma function,

$$\frac{n!}{(n-2\varrho)!} 2^{-2\varrho}$$

$$= \frac{\Gamma(\tfrac{1}{2}n+\tfrac{1}{2})}{\Gamma(\tfrac{1}{2}n+\tfrac{1}{2}-\varrho)} \frac{\Gamma(\tfrac{1}{2}n+1)}{\Gamma(\tfrac{1}{2}n+1-\varrho)} = (\tfrac{1}{2}-\tfrac{1}{2}n)_\varrho (-\tfrac{1}{2}n)_\varrho,$$

so that

$$P_n(\mu) = \frac{(\tfrac{1}{2})_n}{n!} (2\mu)^n \sum_{\varrho=0}^{\infty} \frac{(\tfrac{1}{2}-\tfrac{1}{2}n)_\varrho(-\tfrac{1}{2}n)_\varrho}{\varrho!(\tfrac{1}{2}-n)_\varrho} \left(\frac{1}{\mu^2}\right)^\varrho,$$

a result which may be written in the form

$$P_n(\mu) = \frac{(2\mu)^n(\tfrac{1}{2})_n}{n!} \,_2F_1\left(\tfrac{1}{2}-\tfrac{1}{2}n, \ -\tfrac{1}{2}n; \ \tfrac{1}{2}-n; \ \frac{1}{\mu^2}\right). \quad (13.4b)$$

Putting $\mu = 1$ in equation (13.2) and equating co-efficients of h^n we find that

$$P_n(1) = 1 \qquad\qquad (13.5a)$$

for all values of n. Similarly if we put $\mu = -1$ in (13.2) we derive the result

$$P_n(-1) = (-1)^n \qquad\qquad (13.5b)$$

which is a particular case of the result

$$P_n(-\mu) = (-1)^n P_n(\mu). \qquad\qquad (13.6)$$

Equation (13.4) gives $P_n(\cos\theta)$ as a polynomial in $\cos\theta$ of degree n so that it should be possible to express $P_n(\cos\theta)$ in terms of cosines of multiples of θ. Instead of attempting to do this by substituting the appropriate expression for $\cos^r\theta$ in (13.4) we begin afresh with the definition (13.2). Writing $(1-2\cos\theta h+h^2)$ in the form $(1-e^{i\theta}h)(1-e^{-i\theta}h)$ we find that

$$\sum_{n=0}^{\infty} P_n(\cos\theta)h^n = (1-he^{i\theta})^{-\frac{1}{2}}(1-he^{-i\theta})^{-\frac{1}{2}}$$

$$= \sum_{r=0}^{\infty} \sum_{s=0}^{\infty} \frac{\Gamma(r+\tfrac{1}{2})\Gamma(s+\tfrac{1}{2})}{\Gamma(\tfrac{1}{2})\Gamma(\tfrac{1}{2})r!s!} h^{r+s}e^{i(r-s)\theta}.$$

Equating the coefficients of h^n we find that

$$P_n(\cos \theta) = \sum_{r=0}^{n} \frac{\Gamma(\frac{1}{2}+r)\Gamma(\frac{1}{2}+n-r)}{\Gamma(\frac{1}{2})\Gamma(\frac{1}{2})r!(n-r)!} e^{i(2r-n)\theta}.$$

Using the duplication formula, we see that

$$\frac{\Gamma(\frac{1}{2}+r)\Gamma(\frac{1}{2}+n-r)}{\Gamma(\frac{1}{2})\Gamma(\frac{1}{2})} = \frac{1}{2^{2n}} \frac{(2n-2r)!(2r)!}{r!(n-r)!},$$

so that

$$P_n(\cos \theta) = \frac{1}{2^{2n}} \sum_{r=0}^{n} \frac{(2n-2r)!(2r)!}{(r!)^2\{(n-r)!\}^2} e^{i(2r-n)\theta},$$

from which it follows immediately that

$$P_{2n}(\cos \theta)$$
$$= \frac{\{(2n)!\}^2}{2^{4n}(n!)^4} + \frac{1}{2^{4n-1}} \sum_{r=0}^{n-1} \frac{(4n-2r)!(2r)!}{(r!)^2\{(2n-r)!\}^2} \cos(2n-2r)\theta,$$
$$\tag{13.7}$$

and

$$P_{2n+1}(\cos \theta)$$
$$= \frac{1}{2^{4n+1}} \sum_{r=0}^{n} \frac{(4n+2-2r)!(2r)!}{(r!)^2\{(2n+1-r)!\}^2} \cos(2n-2r+1)\theta. \tag{13.8}$$

From these last two equations we may derive a general result of some importance. We may write

$$P_n(\cos \theta) = \sum_{r=0}^{p} c_r \cos(n-2r)\theta, \tag{13.9}$$

where $p = \frac{1}{2}n$ or $\frac{1}{2}n - \frac{1}{2}$ according as n is even or odd. In particular

$$P_n(1) = \sum_{r=0}^{p} c_r,$$

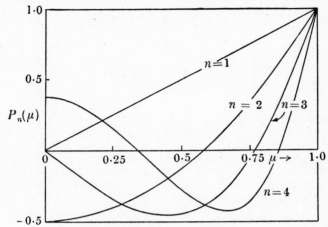

Fig. 5.   Variation of $P_n(\mu)$ with μ.

$$| P_n(\cos \theta) | \leqq 1. \tag{13.10}$$

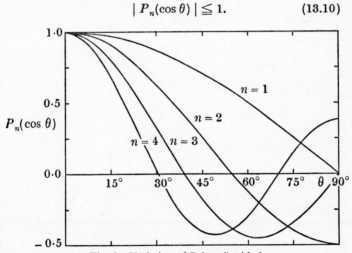

Fig. 6.   Variation of $P_n(\cos \theta)$ with θ.

so that from (13.5)

$$1 = \sum_{r=0}^{p} c_r .$$

Now, from equation (13.9) we have

$$\left| P_n(\cos \theta) \right| \leqq \sum_{r=0}^{p} c_r.$$

and therefore

$$\left| P_n(\cos \theta) \right| \leqq 1. \qquad (13.10)$$

The variation of $P_n(\mu)$ with μ for a few values of n is shown in fig. 5. Since, in most physical problems, the Legendre polynomial involved is usually $P_n(\cos \theta)$ we have shown in fig. 6 the variation of this function with θ. Numerical values may be obtained from *Tables of Associated Legendre Functions* (Columbia University Press, 1945).

§ **14. Recurrence relations for the Legendre polynomials.** If we differentiate both sides of equation (13.2) with respect to h we have

$$\frac{\mu-h}{(1-2\mu h+h^2)^{\frac{3}{2}}} = \sum_{n=0}^{\infty} nh^{n-1}P_n(\mu), \quad \left| \mu \right| < 1,$$

which may be written in the form

$$(\mu-h) \sum_{n=0}^{\infty} h^n P_n(\mu) = (1-2\mu h+h^2) \sum_{n=0}^{\infty} nh^{n-1}P_n(\mu). \quad (14.1)$$

Equating coefficients of h^n we have

$$\mu P_n(\mu) - P_{n-1}(\mu)$$
$$= (n+1)P_{n+1}(\mu) - 2n\mu P_n(\mu) + (n-1)P_{n-1}(\mu),$$

which reduces to

$$(n+1)P_{n+1}(\mu) - (2n+1)\mu P_n(\mu) + nP_{n-1}(\mu) = 0. \quad (14.2)$$

This relation has been proved to hold for $\left| \mu \right| < 1$ but since the left-hand side is a polynomial in μ, it must hold for *all* values of μ.

On the other hand, if we differentiate both sides of equation (13.2) with respect to μ we obtain the relation

$$\frac{h}{(1-2\mu h+h^2)^{\frac{3}{2}}} = \sum_{n=0}^{\infty} h^n P_n'(\mu). \tag{14.3}$$

Combining equations (14.1) and (14.3), we have

$$(\mu-h)\sum_{n=0}^{\infty} h^n P_n'(\mu) = \sum_{n=0}^{\infty} nh^n P_n(\mu),$$

so that equating the coefficients of h^n we obtain the relation

$$\mu P_n'(\mu) - P_{n-1}'(\mu) = nP_n(\mu), \tag{14.4}$$

and since each side is a polynomial in μ this relation holds for all values of μ.

If now we differentiate equation (14.2) with respect to μ we obtain the relation

$$(n+1)P_{n+1}'(\mu) - (2n+1)P_n(\mu)$$
$$-(2n+1)\mu P_n'(\mu) + nP_{n-1}'(\mu) = 0. \tag{14.5}$$

Eliminating $P_n'(\mu)$ from (14.4) and (14.5) we see that

$$P_{n+1}'(\mu) - P_{n-1}'(\mu) = (2n+1)P_n(\mu). \tag{14.6}$$

Subtracting (14.4) from (14.6) we obtain the recurrence relation

$$P_{n+1}'(\mu) - \mu P_n'(\mu) = (n+1)P_n(\mu). \tag{14.7}$$

The differentiations with respect to h and μ under the summation sign is justified by the fact that the series on the right-hand side of equation (13.2) is uniformly convergent for all real or complex values of h and μ which satisfy the relation $|\mu| \leqq 1$, $|h| < \sqrt{2}-1$.

§ 15. The formulae of Murphy and Rodrigues. From

E

the expansion (13.2) it follows immediately that

$$\sum_{n=0}^{\infty} h^n \frac{d^r}{d\mu^r} P_n(\mu) = \frac{d^r}{d\mu^r} (1-2\mu h+h^2)^{-\frac{1}{2}}$$

$$= 2^r h^r \frac{\Gamma(r+\frac{1}{2})}{\Gamma(\frac{1}{2})} (1-2\mu h+h^2)^{-r-\frac{1}{2}}.$$

Substituting the value $\mu = 1$ we see that

$$\sum_{n=0}^{\infty} P_n^{(r)}(1)h^n = 2^r \frac{\Gamma(r+\frac{1}{2})}{\Gamma(\frac{1}{2})} h^r(1-h)^{-(2r+1)}$$

$$= 2^r \frac{\Gamma(r+\frac{1}{2})}{\Gamma(\frac{1}{2})} h^r \sum_{s=0}^{\infty} \frac{\Gamma(1+2r+s)}{\Gamma(1+2r)s!} h^s$$

where $P_n^{(r)}(\mu)$ denotes $d^r P_n(\mu)/d\mu^r$.

Equating coefficients of h^n we see that $P_n^{(r)}(1) = 0$ if $r>n$, as is obvious from the fact that $P_n(\mu)$ is a polynomial of degree n in μ, and that

$$P_n^{(r)}(1) = 2^r \frac{\Gamma(r+\frac{1}{2})}{\Gamma(\frac{1}{2})} \frac{\Gamma(1+n+r)}{\Gamma(1+2r)(n-r)!},$$

From the duplication formula for the gamma function

$$\frac{2^r\Gamma(r+\frac{1}{2})}{\Gamma(\frac{1}{2})\Gamma(1+2r)} = \frac{1}{r!2^r} = \frac{1}{(1)_r 2^r},$$

and from example 9 (iii) of Chapter I,

$$\frac{\Gamma(1+n+r)}{(n-r)!} = (-1)^r(n+1)_r(-n)_r,$$

so that

$$P_n^{(r)}(1) = (-1)^r \frac{(n+1)_r(-n)_r}{(1)_r 2^r}. \tag{15.1}$$

Now, by Taylor's theorem

$$P_n(\mu) = \sum_{r=0}^{\infty} \frac{(\mu-1)^r}{r!} P_n^{(r)}(1).$$

Substituting the expression (15.1) in this expansion we obtain the relation

$$P_n(\mu) = \sum_{r=0}^{\infty} \frac{(-n)_r(n+1)_r}{(1)_r r!} \left(\frac{1-\mu}{2}\right)^r$$

which gives **Murphy's formula,**

$$P_n(\mu) = {}_2F_1\left(-n,\, n+1;\, 1;\, \frac{1-\mu}{2}\right), \tag{15.2}$$

for the Legendre polynomial $P_n(\mu)$.

If now we put $\alpha = 1$ in example 5 of Chapter II we see that equation (15.2) is equivalent to

$$P_n(\mu) = \frac{1}{2^n n!} \frac{d^n}{d\mu^n} (\mu^2-1)^n, \tag{15.3}$$

which is **Rodrigues' formula** for the Legendre polynomial.

Rodrigues' formula is of great use in the evaluation of definite integrals involving Legendre polynomials. Consider, for instance, the integral

$$I = \int_{-1}^{1} f(x)P_n(x)dx. \tag{15.4}$$

By Rodrigues' formula we may write this integral as

$$\frac{1}{2^n n!} \int_{-1}^{1} f(x) \frac{d^n}{dx^n} (x^2-1)^n dx,$$

and an integration by parts gives

$$\frac{1}{2^n n!} \left[\frac{d^{n-1}}{dx^{n-1}} (x^2-1)^n\right]_{-1}^{1}$$
$$- \frac{1}{2^n n!} \int_{-1}^{1} f'(x) \frac{d^{n-1}}{dx^{n-1}} \{(x^2-1)^n\}dx.$$

The square bracket vanishes at both limits so that we have

$$I = - \frac{1}{2^n n!} \int_{-1}^{1} f'(x) \frac{d^{n-1}}{dx^{n-1}} \{(x^2-1)^n\} dx.$$

Continuing this process we find that

$$I = \frac{(-1)^n}{2^n n!} \int_{-1}^{1} (x^2-1)^n f^{(n)}(x) dx. \tag{15.5}$$

For example if $f(x) = P_m(x)$, $m < n$, $f^{(n)}(x) = 0$ and so $I = 0$. In other words

$$\int_{-1}^{1} P_m(x) P_n(x) dx = 0, \quad (m \neq n). \tag{15.6}$$

If $f(x) = P_n(x)$ then

$$f^{(n)}(x) = \frac{1}{2^n n!} \frac{d^{2n}}{dx^{2n}} (x^2-1)^n$$

$$= \frac{(2n)!}{2^n n!}.$$

Hence

$$\int_{-1}^{1} \{P_n(x)\}^2 dx = \frac{(2n)!}{2^{2n}(n!)^2} \int_{-1}^{1} (1-x^2)^n dx$$

$$= \frac{(2n)!}{2^{2n}(n!)^2} \frac{\Gamma(\frac{1}{2})\Gamma(n+1)}{\Gamma(n+\frac{3}{2})}.$$

Making use of the duplication formula for the gamma function we can reduce this to the form

$$\int_{-1}^{1} \{P_n(x)\}^2 dx = \frac{2}{2n+1}. \tag{15.7}$$

A convenient way of combining the results (15.6) and (15.7) is to write

$$\int_{-1}^{1} P_m(x) P_n(x) dx = \frac{2}{2n+1} \delta_{m, n} \tag{15.8}$$

where $\delta_{m,n}$ is the Kronecker delta which takes the value 0 if $m \neq n$ and the value 1 if $m = n$.

Similarly if $f(x) = x^m$, where m is a positive integer, then

$$f^{(n)}(x) = \begin{cases} \dfrac{\Gamma(m+1)}{\Gamma(m-n+1)}\, x^{m-n}, & \text{if } m \geqq n, \\[2mm] 0, & \text{if } m < n, \end{cases}$$

and hence, if $m > n$,

$$\int_{-1}^{1} x^m P_n(x)\,dx = \frac{\Gamma(m+1)}{2^n \Gamma(m-n+1)\, n!} \int_{-1}^{1} x^{m-n}(1-x^2)^n\,dx.$$

If $m-n$ is an odd integer the integral on the right is zero while if $m-n$ is an even integer it has the value

$$2 \int_{0}^{1} x^{m-n}(1-x^2)^n\,dx = \frac{\Gamma(\tfrac{1}{2}m - \tfrac{1}{2}n + \tfrac{1}{2})\Gamma(n+1)}{\Gamma(\tfrac{1}{2}m + \tfrac{1}{2}n + \tfrac{3}{2})},$$

so that, if m is an integer,

$$\int_{-1}^{1} x^m P_n(x)\,dx$$

$$= \begin{cases} 0, & \text{if } m < n, \\[2mm] \dfrac{m!\,\Gamma(\tfrac{1}{2}m - \tfrac{1}{2}n + \tfrac{1}{2})}{2^n(m-n)!\,\Gamma(\tfrac{1}{2}m + \tfrac{1}{2}n + \tfrac{3}{2})}, & \text{if } m-n \geqq 0 \text{ is even,} \quad (15.9) \\[2mm] 0, & \text{if } m-n > 0 \text{ is odd.} \end{cases}$$

If $m = n$ the result is

$$\int_{-1}^{1} x^n P_n(x)\,dx = \frac{1}{2^n} \int_{-1}^{1} (1-x^2)^n\,dx$$

$$= \frac{1}{2^n} \frac{\Gamma(\tfrac{1}{2})\Gamma(n+1)}{\Gamma(n+\tfrac{3}{2})}$$

which, on account of the duplication formula, is equivalent to

$$\int_{-1}^{1} x^n P_n(x)\,dx = \frac{2^{n+1}(n!)^2}{(2n+1)!}. \tag{15.10}$$

§ 16. **Series of Legendre polynomials.** In certain problems of potential theory it is desirable to be able to express a given function in the form of a series of Legendre polynomials. We can readily show that this is possible in the case in which the given function is a simple polynomial. For example, from the equations (13.4a) we have

$$1 = P_0(\mu),$$
$$\mu = P_1(\mu),$$
$$\mu^2 = \tfrac{1}{3} + \tfrac{2}{3}P_2(\mu) = \tfrac{1}{3}P_0(\mu) + \tfrac{2}{3}P_2(\mu),$$
$$\mu^3 = \tfrac{3}{5}\mu + \tfrac{2}{5}P_3(\mu) = \tfrac{3}{5}P_1(\mu) + \tfrac{2}{5}P_3(\mu),$$

so that any cubic $c_0\mu^3 + c_1\mu^2 + c_2\mu + c_3$ can be written as the series

$$\frac{2c_0}{5}P_3(\mu) + \frac{2c_1}{3}P_2(\mu) + \left(\frac{3c_0}{5} + c_2\right)P_1(\mu) + \left(\frac{2c_1}{3} + c_3\right)P_0(\mu).$$

It is obvious that we could proceed in this way for a polynomial of any given degree n though if n were large the arithmetic involved might become cumbersome. Since $P_n(\mu)$ is a polynomial of degree n in μ, it emerges as a result of an extension of the above argument that *any* polynomial of degree n in μ can be expressed as a series of the type

$$\sum_{r=0}^{n} c_r P_r(\mu), \quad (-1 \leqq \mu \leqq 1). \tag{16.1}$$

The problem which now arises is that of expressing *any* function $f(\mu)$, defined in the interval $-1 \leqq \mu \leqq 1$, as a series of Legendre functions of the form

$$\sum_{r=0}^{\infty} c_r P_r(\mu). \tag{16.2}$$

If it is assumed that the infinite series (16.2) converges uniformly in the range $(-1, 1)$ to the sum $f(\mu)$, we may multiply the terms of the series by $P_n(\mu)$ and integrate term by term with respect to μ over the range $(-1, 1)$ to obtain the relation

$$\int_{-1}^{1} f(\mu)P_n(\mu)d\mu = \sum_{r=0}^{\infty} c_r \int_{-1}^{1} P_r(\mu)P_n(\mu)d\mu$$

and by equation (15.8) the sum on the right-hand side is equal to

$$\sum_{r=0}^{\infty} c_r \frac{2}{2n+1} \delta_{r,\,n} = \frac{2c_n}{2n+1}$$

which shows that the series

$$\sum_{r=0}^{\infty} (n+\tfrac{1}{2})P_n(\mu) \int_{-1}^{1} f(v)P_n(v)dv \qquad (16.3)$$

converges uniformly to the sum $f(\mu)$ in the range $(-1, 1)$. The series (16.3) is called the **Legendre series** of the function $f(\mu)$. We shall not discuss here the conditions which must be satisfied by the function $f(\mu)$ if this series is to be uniformly convergent; for such a discussion the reader is referred to Chapter VII of E. W. Hobson, *The Theory of Spherical and Ellipsoidal Harmonics* (Cambridge University Press, 1931).

The possibility of expanding a function in the form of a series of type (16.2) is a consequence of the relation (15.6). In the theory of special functions we frequently encounter sequences of functions $\phi_1(x)$, $\phi_2(x)$, ..., $\phi_n(x)$, ... which have the property

$$\int_{a}^{b} \phi_m(x)\phi_n(x)dx = 0, \qquad (m \neq n). \qquad (16.4)$$

We then say that the functions $\phi_r(x)$, $(r = 1, 2, ...)$, form an **orthogonal sequence** for the interval (a, b). If, in addition, the functions are such that

$$\int_a^b \{\phi_n(x)\}^2 dx = 1, \tag{16.5}$$

for all values of n, we say that the functions of the sequence are **normalised**, and form an **orthonormal** set. Given a set of orthogonal functions it is obviously a simple matter to construct a normalised sequence. For example we see from equation (15.8) that the sequence of functions $P_n(x)$, $(n = 0, 1, 2, \ldots)$ is orthogonal but not normalised. By multiplying each function by $\sqrt{(n+\frac{1}{2})}$ we find that the functions

$$(n+\tfrac{1}{2})^{\frac{1}{2}} P_n(x) \tag{16.6}$$

form a sequence of normalised orthogonal functions in the interval $(-1, 1)$.

There is another property of importance which such a sequence of functions may possess. If there is no integrable function $\psi(x)$, different from zero, such that

$$\int_a^b \psi(x)\phi_n(x)dx = 0 \tag{16.7}$$

for *all* values of n we say that the sequence is a **complete** orthogonal sequence. It may be shown in the case of the functions (16.6) † by considering the Fourier coefficients of $\psi(x/\pi)P_n(x/\pi)$ in $(-\pi, \pi)$ that if (16.7) holds this function is a null-function and hence that $\psi(x)$ is a null-function in $(-1, 1)$. In other words it can be shown that the functions (16.6) form a complete sequence of normalised orthogonal functions.

§ 17. Legendre's differential equation.   If we write

$$v = (\mu^2 - 1)^n$$

then it is readily shown that

$$(1-\mu^2)\frac{dv}{d\mu} + 2\mu n v = 0$$

† E. W. Hobson, *op. cit.*, p. 40.

and if we differentiate this equation $n+1$ times using Leibnitz's theorem we find that

$$(1-\mu^2)\frac{d^{n+2}v}{d\mu^{n+2}} - 2\mu\frac{d^{n+1}v}{d\mu^{n+1}} + n(n+1)\frac{d^n v}{d\mu^n} = 0$$

which when written in the form

$$\left\{(1-\mu^2)\frac{d^2}{d\mu^2} - 2\mu\frac{d}{d\mu} + n(n+1)\right\}\left(\frac{d^n v}{d\mu^n}\right) = 0$$

shows that $d^n(\mu^2-1)^n/d\mu^n$ is a solution of the differential equation

$$(1-\mu^2)\frac{d^2 y}{d\mu^2} - 2\mu\frac{dy}{d\mu} + n(n+1)y = 0 \qquad (17.1)$$

so that we conclude from Rodrigues' formula (15.3) that when n is an integer $P_n(\mu)$ is one solution of the equation (17.1). This equation, which we shall now consider in a little more detail, is called **Legendre's differential equation.** We saw in example 1 of Chapter I how such an equation arises in the solution of Laplace's equation when solutions of the type $R(r)\Theta(\cos\theta)$, i.e. $m = 0$, are sought.

It is obvious by inspection that the point $\mu = 0$ is an ordinary point of the equation (17.1). Writing the equation in the form

$$(\mu-1)^2\frac{d^2 y}{d\mu^2} + (\mu-1)\frac{2\mu}{\mu+1}\frac{dy}{d\mu} - \frac{n(n+1)}{\mu+1}(\mu-1)y = 0$$

and observing that in the notation of equation (3.1) with $a = 1$,

$$p(\mu) = \frac{1+(\mu-1)}{1+\frac{1}{2}(\mu-1)} = 1 + \tfrac{1}{2}(\mu-1) - \tfrac{1}{4}(\mu-1)^2 \ldots,$$

$$q(\mu) = -\tfrac{1}{2}n(n+1)\frac{\mu-1}{1+\frac{1}{2}(\mu-1)}$$

$$= -\tfrac{1}{2}n(n+1)\{(\mu-1) - \tfrac{1}{2}(\mu-1)^2 + \ldots\},$$

we see that $\mu = 1$ is a regular singular point with indicial equation $\varrho^2 = 0$.

Furthermore in the notation of equation (4.2)

$$\alpha(\mu) \equiv \frac{-2\mu}{1-\mu^2}, \quad \beta(\mu) = \frac{n(n+1)}{1-\mu^2},$$

so that as $\mu \to \infty$

$$\alpha(\mu) \sim \frac{2}{\mu}, \quad \beta(\mu) \sim -\frac{n(n+1)}{\mu^2},$$

showing that the point $\mu = \infty$ is a regular singular point with indicial equation $\{\varrho - (n+1)\} (\varrho + n) = 0$. We thus see that the equation is defined by the scheme

$$y = P \left\{ \begin{array}{ccc} -1 & \infty & 1 \\ 0 & n+1 & 0 \quad \mu \\ 0 & -n & 0 \end{array} \right\}. \qquad (17.2)$$

If, however, we put

$$x = \tfrac{1}{2}(1-\mu)$$

in equation (17.1) we find that it reduces to the form

$$x(1-x) \frac{d^2y}{dx^2} + (1-2x) \frac{dy}{dx} + n(n+1)y = 0, \qquad (17.3)$$

which is equation (8.1) with $\alpha = n+1$, $\beta = -n$ and $\gamma = 1$, so that the scheme (17.2) is equivalent to the scheme

$$y = P \left\{ \begin{array}{ccc} 0 & \infty & 1 \\ 0 & n+1 & 0 \quad \tfrac{1}{2}-\tfrac{1}{2}\mu \\ 0 & -n & 0 \end{array} \right\}. \qquad (17.4)$$

It should be noticed that the values along the top row are those assumed by $\tfrac{1}{2} - \tfrac{1}{2}\mu$, not by μ.

We consider first the solution corresponding to the singular point at infinity. We write

$$y_1(\mu) = \mu^n \sum_{\nu=0}^{\infty} c_\nu \mu^{-\nu}$$

which on substitution into (17.1) leads to the recurrence relation

$$(n-v+2)(n-v+1)c_{v-2} = -v(2n+1-v)c_v.$$

On taking $c_0 = 1$ we obtain the solution

$$y_1(\mu) = \mu^n - \frac{n(n-1)}{2 \cdot (2n-1)} \mu^{n-2} + \frac{n(n-1)(n-2)(n-3)}{2 \cdot 4 \cdot (2n-1)(2n-3)} \mu^{n-4} + \dots$$

$$= \mu^n \left\{ 1 + \frac{(-\tfrac{1}{2}n)(\tfrac{1}{2}-\tfrac{1}{2}n)}{1 \cdot (\tfrac{1}{2}-n)} \frac{1}{\mu^2} \right.$$

$$\left. + \frac{(-\tfrac{1}{2}n)(-\tfrac{1}{2}n+1)(\tfrac{1}{2}-\tfrac{1}{2}n)(\tfrac{1}{2}-\tfrac{1}{2}n+1)}{1 \cdot 2(\tfrac{1}{2}-n)(\tfrac{1}{2}-n+1)} \frac{1}{\mu^4} + \dots \right\}$$

which may be written in the form

$$y_1(\mu) = \mu^n \, {}_2F_1\left(-\tfrac{1}{2}n, \tfrac{1}{2}-\tfrac{1}{2}n; \tfrac{1}{2}-n; \frac{1}{\mu^2} \right). \quad (17.5)$$

Also, if we write for the second solution

$$y_2(\mu) = \mu^{-n-1} \sum_{v=0}^{\infty} d_v \mu^{-v}$$

we find that

$$y_2(\mu) = \mu^{-n-1} + \frac{(n+1)(n+2)}{2 \cdot (2n+3)} \mu^{-n-3}$$

$$+ \frac{(n+1)(n+2)(n+3)(n+4)}{2 \cdot 4 \cdot (2n+3)(2n+5)} \mu^{-n-5} + \dots$$

$$= \frac{1}{\mu^{n+1}} \, {}_2F_1\left(\tfrac{1}{2}n+\tfrac{1}{2}, \tfrac{1}{2}n+1; n+\tfrac{3}{2}; \frac{1}{\mu^2} \right), \quad (17.6)$$

provided n is any number other than a negative integer or half a negative integer.

These solutions are valid for *all* values of n for which the ${}_2F_1$ series have a meaning, not only for integral values of n. If n is an integer the series $y_1(\mu)$ terminates—in other words, $y_1(\mu)$ is a polynomial of degree n in μ. If we multiply this polynomial by

$$\frac{(2n)!}{2^n(n!)^2}$$

we obtain the Legendre polynomial of degree n (equation (13.4b) above).

On the other hand the series for $y_2(\mu)$ does not terminate when $n > -1$ so there is no point in restricting n to be an integer. This series solution when multiplied by a factor

$$\frac{\Gamma(\tfrac{1}{2})\Gamma(n+1)}{2^{n+1}\Gamma(n+\tfrac{3}{2})}$$

gives the function

$$
\begin{aligned}
&Q_n(\mu) \\
&= \frac{\Gamma(\tfrac{1}{2})\Gamma(n+1)}{2^{n+1}\Gamma(n+\tfrac{3}{2})}\, \mu^{-n-1}\, {}_2F_1\left(\tfrac{1}{2}n+\tfrac{1}{2},\ \tfrac{1}{2}n+1;\ n+\tfrac{3}{2};\ \frac{1}{\mu^2}\right).
\end{aligned}
\tag{17.7}
$$

The function

$$P_n(\mu) = \frac{\Gamma(2n+1)}{2^n\{\Gamma(n+1)\}^2}\, \mu^n\, {}_2F_1\left(-\tfrac{1}{2}n,\ \tfrac{1}{2}-\tfrac{1}{2}n;\ \tfrac{1}{2}-n;\ \frac{1}{\mu^2}\right) \tag{17.8}$$

is a solution of the Legendre equation (17.4) even when n is not an integer and it reduces to the Legendre polynomial when n is an integer. We shall continue to denote it by $P_n(\mu)$ but when n is not an integer shall refer to it as the **Legendre function of the first kind of degree n**. The function $Q_n(\mu)$ defined by equation (17.7) will be referred to as the **Legendre function of the second kind of degree n**; even when n is an integer it is not a polynomial.

With these definitions we may write the solution of Legendre's equation (17.1) as

$$y = AP_n(\mu) + BQ_n(\mu) \tag{17.9}$$

($|\mu| > 1$). In some problems we know that the solution should be a polynomial in μ; in that case we must take the solution to the form $y = A P_n(\mu)$.

The variation of $Q_n(\mu)$ with μ may be computed easily from equation (17.7) when $\mu > 1$. Tables calculated in this way are contained in the volume quoted at the end of § 13. The following fig. 7, which was prepared from these

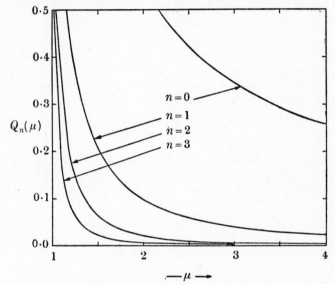

Fig. 7. Variation of $Q_n(\mu)$ with μ.

tables, shows the variation of $Q_n(\mu)$ with μ for a few values of n.

Since Legendre's equation has a regular singular point at $\mu = 1$ we may on the basis of equation (3.8) take the second solution of Legendre's equation to be proportional to

$$P_n(\mu) \log(\mu - 1) + \Sigma c_r(\mu - 1)^r.$$

The coefficients c_r can now be obtained by substituting

this expression into the differential equation (17.1) and equating to zero coefficients of successive powers of $(\mu-1)$. Instead of proceeding in this way we shall derive this second solution by means of a method due to F. E. Neumann.

§ 18. Neumann's formula for the Legendre functions.

Let us now consider the integral

$$\int_{-1}^{1} \frac{P_n(\xi)d\xi}{\mu-\xi},$$

where $|\mu|>1$, and n is a positive integer. Expanding the denominator by the binomial theorem, we have, for the value of the integral, the series

$$\sum_{s=0}^{\infty} \frac{1}{\mu^{s+1}} \int_{-1}^{1} \xi^s P_n(\xi)d\xi.$$

From equation (15.9), it follows that the integrals in this series are zero if $s \leq n$, or if $s = n+2r$ where r is a positive integer, so that the above series is equivalent to

$$\sum_{r=0}^{\infty} \frac{1}{\mu^{n+1+2r}} \int_{-1}^{1} \xi^{n+2r} P_n(\xi)d\xi,$$

which, by the same formula, is equal to

$$\frac{1}{\mu^{n+1}} \sum_{r=0}^{\infty} \frac{(n+2r)!\,\Gamma(r+\tfrac{1}{2})}{2^n(2r)!\,\Gamma(n+r+\tfrac{3}{2})} \left(\frac{1}{\mu^2}\right)^r.$$

Now from the duplication formula

$$\frac{(n+2r)!\,\Gamma(\tfrac{1}{2}+r)}{2^n(2r)!} = \frac{\Gamma(\tfrac{1}{2}n+\tfrac{1}{2}+r)\Gamma(\tfrac{1}{2}n+1+r)}{r!},$$

so that the series reduces to

$$\frac{1}{\mu^{n+1}} \sum_{r=0}^{\infty} \frac{\Gamma(\tfrac{1}{2}n+\tfrac{1}{2}+r)\Gamma(\tfrac{1}{2}n+1+r)}{\Gamma(n+\tfrac{3}{2}+r)r!} \left(\frac{1}{\mu^2}\right)^r$$

which is equal to

$$\frac{\Gamma(\frac{1}{2}n+\frac{1}{2})\Gamma(\frac{1}{2}n+1)}{\Gamma(n+\frac{3}{2})\mu^{n+1}} \, {}_2F_1\left(\frac{1}{2}n+\frac{1}{2}, \frac{1}{2}n+1; n+\frac{3}{2}; \frac{1}{\mu^2}\right).$$

Noticing that

$$\Gamma(\tfrac{1}{2}n+\tfrac{1}{2})\Gamma(\tfrac{1}{2}n+1)/\Gamma(n+\tfrac{3}{2}) = \Gamma(\tfrac{1}{2})\Gamma(n+1)/2^n\Gamma(n+\tfrac{3}{2}),$$

and comparing the result with equation (17.7) we see that this series is merely $2Q_n(\mu)$. Hence we have shown that if $|\mu| > 1$

$$Q_n(\mu) = \tfrac{1}{2}\int_{-1}^{1}\frac{P_n(\xi)}{\mu-\xi}\,d\xi, \tag{18.1}$$

a result which is known as **Neumann's formula**. Equation (18.1) holds not only for real values of μ greater than 1, but for all values of μ which are not real. For this reason equation (18.1) may be regarded as defining the second solution, $Q_n(\mu)$, of Legendre's equation.

Certain related formulae, due to MacRobert, follow readily from this result. If $|\mu| > 1$ and m is a positive integer then

$$\mu^m Q_n(\mu) - \tfrac{1}{2}\int_{-1}^{1}\frac{\xi^m P_n(\xi)}{\mu-\xi}\,d\xi = \tfrac{1}{2}\int_{-1}^{1}\frac{\mu^m-\xi^m}{\mu-\xi}P_n(\xi)d\xi$$

and the integral on the right is equivalent to the finite sum

$$\tfrac{1}{2}\sum_{r=0}^{m-1}\mu^{m-1-r}\int_{-1}^{1}\xi^r P_n(\xi)d\xi. \tag{18.2}$$

If $m \leq n$ it follows from equation (15.9) that each term of this series vanishes so that we have

$$\mu^m Q_n(\mu) = \tfrac{1}{2}\int_{-1}^{1}\frac{\xi^m P_n(\xi)}{\mu-\xi}\,d\xi \tag{18.3}$$

provided m, n are integers and $m \leq n$.

On the other hand, if $m = n+1$ the series (18.2) reduces

to the single term

$$\tfrac{1}{2} \int_{-1}^{1} \xi^n P_n(\xi) d\xi = \frac{2^n (n!)^2}{(2n+1)!},$$

so that

$$\mu^{n+1} Q_n(\mu) = \tfrac{1}{2} \int_{-1}^{1} \frac{\xi^{n+1} P_n(\xi)}{\mu - \xi} d\xi + \frac{2^n (n!)^2}{(2n+1)!}. \quad (18.4)$$

Now if m is an integer $P_m(\mu)$ is a polynomial of degree m in μ so that it follows from (18.3) by finite summation that, if $m \leq n$,

$$P_m(\mu) Q_n(\mu) = \tfrac{1}{2} \int_{-1}^{1} \frac{P_m(\xi) P_n(\xi)}{\mu - \xi} d\xi. \quad (18.5)$$

Similarly from equation (18.4) and the definition of $P_{n+1}(\mu)$ we have the formula

$$P_{n+1}(\mu) Q_n(\mu) = \tfrac{1}{2} \int_{-1}^{1} \frac{P_{n+1}(\xi) P_n(\xi)}{\mu - \xi} d\xi + \frac{1}{n+1}. \quad (18.6)$$

If we replace n in equation (18.5) by $n+1$ and m by n and subtract from equation (18.6) we obtain the relation

$$P_{n+1}(\mu) Q_n(\mu) - P_n(\mu) Q_{n+1}(\mu) = \frac{1}{n+1}. \quad (18.7)$$

Other formulæ of a similar nature are contained in ex. 24 below.

We shall now make use of Neumann's formula to derive the form of the second solution of Legendre's equation in the neighbourhood of the points $\mu = \pm 1$. From (18.1) we have the result that if $\mu > 1$,

$$Q_n(\mu) = \tfrac{1}{2} P_n(\mu) \log \frac{\mu+1}{\mu-1} - W_{n-1}(\mu), \quad (18.8)$$

where $W_{n-1}(\mu)$ denotes the integral

$$\tfrac{1}{2} \int_{-1}^{1} \frac{P_n(\mu) - P_n(\xi)}{\mu - \xi} d\xi.$$

Now when n is an integer, $P_n(\mu)$ is a polynomial of degree n in μ so that $\{P_n(\mu)-P_n(\xi)\}/(\mu-\xi)$ is a polynomial of degree $n-1$ in μ. Hence $W_{n-1}(\mu)$ is a polynomial of degree $n-1$ in μ.

If we substitute from (18.8) into Legendre's equation (17.1) we find that W_{n-1} satisfies the differential equation

$$(1-\mu^2)W''_{n-1} - 2\mu W'_{n-1} + n(n+1)W_{n-1} = 2P'_n(\mu). \quad (18.9)$$

Now since $W_{n-1}(\mu)$ is a polynomial of degree $n-1$ in μ we may write (cf. § 16 above)

$$W_{n-1}(\mu) = \sum_{r=0}^{n-1} c_r P_r(\mu).$$

Using the fact that

$$P'_n(\mu) = \sum_{r=0}^{p} (2n-4r-1)P_{n-2r-1},$$

where $p = \frac{1}{2}(n-1)$ or $\frac{1}{2}n-1$ according as n is odd or even (which follows from equation (14.6)), and the result

$$(1-\mu^2)P''_r(\mu) - 2\mu P'_r(\mu) + n(n+1)P_r(\mu)$$
$$= (n-r)(n+r+1)P_r(\mu),$$

we find, from equation (18.9), that $c_{n-2s} = 0$, $(s = 0, ..., p)$ and that

$$c_{n-2s-1} = \frac{2n-4s-1}{(2s+1)(n-s)}.$$

Substituting these values in (18.8) we obtain the formula

$$Q_n(\mu) = \frac{1}{2}P_n(\mu)\log\frac{\mu+1}{\mu-1} - \sum_{s=0}^{p} \frac{2n-4s-1}{(2s+1)(n-s)}P_{n-2s-1}(\mu). \quad (18.10)$$

Another expression for $Q_n(\mu)$ may be derived from the fact that both $P_n(\mu)$ and $Q_n(\mu)$ are solutions of Legendre's equation (17.1) so that

$$Q_n(\mu)\frac{d}{d\mu}\{(1-\mu^2)P'_n(\mu)\} - P_n(\mu)\frac{d}{d\mu}\{(1-\mu^2)Q'_n(\mu)\} = 0$$

F

which is equivalent to

$$\frac{d}{d\mu}\left[(1-\mu^2)\{Q_n(\mu)P_n'(\mu) - P_n(\mu)Q_n'(\mu)\}\right] = 0,$$

showing that

$$(1-\mu^2)\{Q_n(\mu)P_n'(\mu) - P_n(\mu)Q_n'(\mu)\} = C, \qquad (18.11)$$

where C is a constant. Now from equations (17.7) and (17.8), we can readily show that for large values of μ

$$P_n'(\mu)Q_n(\mu) \sim \frac{n}{2n+1} \cdot \frac{1}{\mu^2}, \quad Q_n'(\mu)P_n(\mu) \sim -\frac{n+1}{2n+1} \cdot \frac{1}{\mu^2}$$

so that as $\mu \to \infty$ the left-hand side of (18.11) tends to -1, showing that $C = -1$. Writing (18.11) in the form

$$\frac{d}{d\mu}\left\{\frac{Q_n(u)}{P_n(\mu)}\right\} = \frac{-1}{(\mu^2-1)\{P_n(\mu)\}^2}$$

and noting from (17.7) that $Q_n(\mu) \to 0$ as $\mu \to \infty$ we have

$$Q_n(\mu) = P_n(\mu)\int_\mu^\infty \frac{d\xi}{(\xi^2-1)\{P_n(\xi)\}^2}. \qquad (18.12)$$

§ 19. Recurrence relations for the function $Q_n(\mu)$. Recurrence relations for the Legendre function of the second kind can be derived from Neumann's formula (18.1) and the corresponding recurrence relations for the Legendre polynomials $P_n(\mu)$, From the recurrence relation (14.2) and Neumann's formula we have

$$(n+1)Q_{n+1}(\mu) + nQ_{n-1}(\mu) = (n+\tfrac{1}{2})\int_{-1}^1 \frac{\xi P_n(\xi)}{\mu - \xi}\,d\xi.$$

Now

$$\tfrac{1}{2}\int_{-1}^1 \frac{\xi P_n(\xi)}{\mu - \xi}\,d\xi = \mu Q_n(\mu) - \tfrac{1}{2}\int_{-1}^1 P_n(\xi)d\xi.$$

If we write the second term on the right as $\displaystyle\int_{-1}^{1} P_0(\xi)P_n(\xi)d\xi$ we see from (15.6) that it vanishes if $n \neq 0$. Hence we have

$$(n+1)Q_{n+1}(\mu) - (2n+1)\mu Q_n(\mu) + nQ_{n-1}(\mu) = 0 \qquad (19.1)$$

showing that the functions $Q_n(\mu)$ for three consecutive values of n satisfy a relation of the same form as that for the functions $P_n(\mu)$ (equation (14.2) above).

From Neumann's formula (18.1) we have

$$Q_n'(\mu) = -\tfrac{1}{2}\int_{-1}^{1} \frac{P_n(\xi)}{(\mu-\xi)^2}\, d\xi$$

and if we integrate by parts on the right-hand side we find that

$$Q_n'(\mu) = \tfrac{1}{2}\left\{\frac{1}{1-\mu} + \frac{(-1)^n}{1+\mu}\right\} + \tfrac{1}{2}\int_{-1}^{1} \frac{P_n'(\xi)}{\mu-\xi}\, d\xi \, .$$

Hence

$$Q_{n+1}'(\mu) - Q_{n-1}'(\mu) = \tfrac{1}{2}\int_{-1}^{1} \frac{P_{n+1}'(\xi) - P_{n-1}'(\xi)}{\mu-\xi}\, d\xi$$

$$= \tfrac{1}{2}(2n+1)\int_{-1}^{1} \frac{P_n(\xi)}{\mu-\xi}\, d\xi,$$

by virtue of equation (14.6). The integral on the right is $2Q_n(\mu)$ by Neumann's formula so that, finally,

$$Q_{n+1}'(\mu) - Q_{n-1}'(\mu) = (2n+1)Q_n(\mu). \qquad (19.2)$$

§ 20. The use of Legendre functions in potential theory.

In potential theory we have frequently to determine solutions of Laplace's equation $\nabla^2\psi = 0$ which satisfy certain prescribed boundary conditions. If we have a problem in which the natural boundaries are spheres with centre at the origin of coordinates it is natural to employ

polar coordinates r, θ, ϕ. In cases in which there is symmetry about the polar axis ψ will not depend on ϕ so we
may write $\psi = \psi(r, \theta)$. It then follows from example 1
of Chapter I that

$$(A_n r^n + B_n r^{-n-1})v_n$$

will be a solution of Laplace's equation provided that v_n
is a solution of Legendre's equation (17.1). Taking v_n to
be $P_n(\cos \theta) + C_n Q_n(\cos \theta)$ we see that we may write

$$\psi(r, \theta) = \sum_{n=0}^{\infty} (A_n r^n + B_n r^{-n-1})P_n(\cos \theta)$$
$$+ \sum_{n=0}^{\infty} (C_n r^n + D_n r^{-n-1})Q_n(\cos \theta) \qquad (20.1)$$

where the quantities A_n, B_n, C_n, D_n ($n = 0, 1, 2, \ldots$) are all
constants.

Now it is obvious from equation (18.8) that $Q_n(\cos \theta)$
is infinite when $\theta = 0^0$, and we know on physical grounds
that in the case of spherical boundaries ψ remains finite
along the axis $\theta = 0$. Hence we must take $C_n = D_n = 0$
for all values of n and obtain the potential function

$$\psi = \sum_{n=0}^{\infty} (A_n r^n + B_n r^{-n-1})P_n(\cos \theta) \qquad (20.2)$$

which is valid as long as r is neither zero nor infinite, i.e.
if $a \leq r \leq b$ where a and b are finite and non-zero. If the
region under discussion is the interior of a sphere, i.e. if
$0 \leq r \leq a$, then to avoid ψ becoming infinite we must take
B_n to be zero to give

$$\psi = \sum_{n=0}^{\infty} A_n r^n P_n(\cos \theta). \qquad (20.3)$$

On the other hand, if the region being considered lies entirely
outside this sphere, we must take

$$\psi = \sum_{n=0}^{\infty} B_n r^{-n-1} P_n(\cos \theta). \qquad (20.4)$$

Examples of the use of the solutions (20.2, 3, 4) in potential theory are given in Coulson's *Electricity* (Oliver & Boyd, 1948) §§ 75-78, 80; a further example is given below.

The Legendre functions of the second kind, $Q_n(\cos \theta)$, which are absent from problems involving spherical boundaries, enter into the expressions for potential functions appropriate to the space between two coaxial cones. If $0 < \alpha < \theta < \beta < \pi$ we must take a solution of the form (20.1). Suppose, for example, that $\psi = 0$ on $\theta = \alpha$, and $\psi = \Sigma \alpha_n r^n$ on $\theta = \beta$ then we must have

$$A_n P_n(\cos \alpha) + C_n Q_n(\cos \alpha) = 0$$

and

$$A_n P_n(\cos \beta) + C_n Q_n(\cos \beta) = \alpha_n, \quad B_n = D_n = 0,$$

the latter results following from the fact that if $\alpha \neq \beta$, $Q_n(\cos \alpha) P_n(\cos \beta) - P_n(\cos \alpha) Q_n(\cos \beta)$ does not vanish. Solving these equations for A_n and C_n and inserting the solutions in equation (20.1) we find that in the space between the two cones

$$\psi = \sum_{n=0}^{\infty} \alpha_n r^n \left\{ \frac{Q_n(\cos \alpha) P_n(\cos \theta) - P_n(\cos \alpha) Q_n(\cos \theta)}{Q_n(\cos \alpha) P_n(\cos \beta) - P_n(\cos \alpha) Q_n(\cos \beta)} \right\} \quad (20.5)$$

To illustrate the use of the solution (20.1) and of some of the properties of Legendre functions we shall now consider the problem in which an insulated conducting sphere of radius a is placed with its centre at the origin of coordinates in an electric field whose potential is known to be

$$\sum_{n=1}^{\infty} \alpha_n r^n P_n(\cos \theta) \quad (20.6)$$

and we wish to determine the force on the sphere. The conditions to be satisfied by the potential functions ψ are (i) that ψ is a solution of Laplace's equation; (ii) that ψ has the form (20.6) for large values of r; (iii) $\psi = 0$ on $r = a$.

The conditions (i) and (ii) are satisfied if we take

$$\psi = \sum_{n=1}^{\infty} \left(\alpha_n r^n + \frac{B_n}{r^{n+1}} \right) P_n(\cos \theta)$$

and (iii) is satisfied if we write $B_n = -\alpha_n a^{2n+1}$. We therefore have

$$\psi = \sum_{n=1}^{\infty} \alpha_n \left(r^n - \frac{a^{2n+1}}{r^{n+1}} \right) P_n(\cos \theta).$$

The surface density of charge on the conductor is

$$\sigma = -\frac{1}{4\pi} \left(\frac{\partial \psi}{\partial r} \right)_{r=a} = -\frac{1}{4\pi} \sum_{n=1}^{\infty} (2n+1)a^{n-1}\alpha_n P_n(\cos \theta)$$

and since the force per unit area on the conductor is $2\pi\sigma^2$ the resultant force on the sphere is in the $\theta = 0$ direction, and is of magnitude

$$F = \int_0^\pi 2\pi\sigma^2 \, 2\pi a^2 \sin \theta \cos \theta \, d\theta \qquad (20.7)$$

$$= \tfrac{1}{4}a^2 \sum_{n=1}^{\infty} \sum_{m=1}^{\infty} \alpha_m \alpha_n a^{m+n-2} I_{mn}$$

where I_{mn} denotes the integral

$$(2n+1)(2m+1) \int_0^\pi \cos \theta \sin \theta \, P_m(\cos \theta)P_n(\cos \theta)d\theta.$$

Changing the variable of integration to $\mu = \cos \theta$ and using the recurrence relation (14.2) we find that

$$I_{mn} = (2m+1) \left\{ (n+1) \int_{-1}^1 P_m(\mu)P_{n+1}(\mu)d\mu \right.$$

$$\left. + n \int_{-1}^1 P_m(\mu)P_{n-1}(\mu)d\mu \right\}$$

and by the orthogonality property (15.8) this reduces to

the form

$$I_{mn} = 2(n+1)\delta_{m,\,n+1} + 2n\delta_{m,\,n-1}. \qquad (20.8)$$

Substituting from (20.8) into (20.7) we find that the total force on the sphere is

$$F = \sum_{n=1}^{\infty} (n+1)\alpha_n\alpha_{n+1}a^{2n+1}.$$

§ **21. Legendre's associated functions.** We saw in example 1 of Chapter I that the solution of Laplace's equation in spherical polar coordinates reduces to the solution of the ordinary differential equation,

$$(1-\mu^2)\frac{d^2\Theta}{d\mu^2} - 2\mu\frac{d\Theta}{d\mu} + \left\{n(n+1) - \frac{m^2}{1-\mu^2}\right\}\Theta = 0 \qquad (21.1)$$

which reduces to Legendre's equation when $m = 0$. This equation is known as **Legendre's associated equation.** To solve this equation we may write

$$\Theta = (\mu^2 - 1)^{-\frac{1}{2}m}y. \qquad (21.2)$$

Substituting this expression in the differential equation we find that y satisfies the equation

$$(1-\mu^2)\frac{d^2y}{d\mu^2} - 2(1-m)\mu\frac{dy}{d\mu} + (n+m)(n-m+1)y = 0$$

and differentiating this equation m times with respect to μ by Leibnitz's theorem we find that

$$\left\{(1-\mu^2)\frac{d^2}{d\mu^2} - 2\mu\frac{d}{d\mu} + n(n+1)\right\}\frac{d^m y}{d\mu^m} = 0 \qquad (21.3)$$

showing that if $d^m y/d\mu^m$ is a solution of Legendre's equation (17.1) the function Θ, defined by equation (21.2), is a solution of Legendre's associated equation (21.1).

Similarly if we put $\Theta = (\mu^2 - 1)^{\frac{1}{2}m}y$ in equation (21.1) we find that

$$(1-\mu^2)\frac{d^2y}{d\mu^2} - 2(1+m)\mu\frac{dy}{d\mu} + (n-m)(n+m+1)y = 0. \quad (21.4)$$

If now we differentiate equation (17.1) m times with respect to μ we obtain the equation

$$\left\{(1-\mu^2)\frac{d^2}{d\mu^2} - 2(1+m)\mu\frac{d}{d\mu} + (n-m)(n+m+1)\right\}\frac{d^my}{d\mu^m} = 0$$

showing that if $y(\mu)$ is a solution of Legendre's equation then

$$(\mu^2-1)^{\frac{1}{2}m}\frac{d^my}{d\mu^m} \quad (21.5)$$

is a solution of Legendre's associated equation (21.1).

Taking the two solutions of Legendre's equation to be $P_n(\mu)$ and $Q_n(\mu)$ it follows from (21.5) that the functions

$$P_n^m(\mu) = (\mu^2-1)^{\frac{1}{2}m}\frac{d^mP_n(\mu)}{d\mu^m},$$

$$Q_n^m(\mu) = (\mu^2-1)^{\frac{1}{2}m}\frac{d^mQ_n(\mu)}{d\mu^m} \quad (21.6)$$

are solutions of Legendre's associated equation. As a consequence of equation (21.3) we see that so also are the functions

$$P_n^{-m}(\mu) = (\mu^2-1)^{-\frac{1}{2}m}\int_1^\mu\int_1^\xi\cdots\int_1^\xi P_n(\xi)(d\xi)^m \quad (21.7)$$

and

$$Q_n^{-m}(\mu) = (\mu^2-1)^{-\frac{1}{2}m}\int_\infty^\mu\int_\infty^\xi\cdots\int_\infty^\xi Q_n(\xi)(d\xi)^m. \quad (21.8)$$

It is an immediate generalisation of (6.5) that

$$\frac{d^m}{dx^m}\,_2F_1(\alpha, \beta; \gamma; x) = \frac{(\alpha)_m(\beta)_m}{(\gamma)_m}\,_2F_1(\alpha+m, \beta+m; \gamma+m; x)$$

so that using Murphy's form (15.2) for $P_n(\mu)$ we see that

$$\frac{d^m}{d\mu^m} P_n(\mu) = \frac{(-n)_m(n+1)_m}{(-2)^m m!}$$
$$_2F_1\left(m-n,\ n+m+1;\ m+1;\ \frac{1-\mu}{2}\right).$$

Hence $P_n^m(\mu)$ as defined in (21.6) may be written in the form

$$P_n^m(\mu) = \frac{\Gamma(n+m+1)}{2^m m!\Gamma(n-m+1)}(\mu^2-1)^{\frac{1}{2}m}$$
$$\times\ _2F_1\left(m-n,\ n+m+1;\ m+1;\ \frac{1-\mu}{2}\right). \quad (21.9)$$

Other expressions for the first of the two functions (21.6) can be easily derived. If we make use of the result (7.4) we see that

$$P_n^m(\mu) = \frac{\Gamma(n+m+1)}{2^n m!\Gamma(n-m+1)}(\mu+1)^{n-\frac{1}{2}m}(\mu-1)$$
$$\times\ _2F_1\left(m-n,\ -n;\ m+1;\ \frac{\mu-1}{\mu+1}\right) \quad (21.10)$$

and similarly, if we make use of relation (7.6) we may derive the expression

$$P_n^m(\mu) = \frac{\Gamma(n+m+1)}{m!\Gamma(n-m+1)}\left(\frac{\mu-1}{\mu+1}\right)^{\frac{1}{2}m}$$
$$\times\ _2F_1\left(n+1,\ -n;\ m+1;\ \frac{1-\mu}{2}\right). \quad (21.11)$$

From Rodrigues' formula (15.3) we derive the simple expression

$$P_n^m(\mu) = \frac{1}{2^n n!}(\mu^2-1)^{\frac{1}{2}m}\frac{d^{m+n}}{d\mu^{m+n}}(\mu^2-1)^n. \quad (21.12)$$

The simple differentiation

$$\frac{d^m}{d\mu^m}\mu^{-n-1-2r} = (-1)^m \frac{\Gamma(m+n+1+2r)}{\Gamma(n+1+2r)}\mu^{-m-n-1-2r}$$

may (because of the duplication formula) be written in the form

$$\Gamma(n+1)\frac{d^m}{d\mu^m}\left\{\frac{(\tfrac{1}{2}n+\tfrac{1}{2})_r(\tfrac{1}{2}n+1)_r}{\mu^{n+1+2r}}\right\}$$

$$= (-1)^m\Gamma(m+n+1)\frac{(\tfrac{1}{2}m+\tfrac{1}{2}n+\tfrac{1}{2})_r(\tfrac{1}{2}m+\tfrac{1}{2}n+1)_r}{\mu^{m+n+1+2r}},$$

showing that, by term-by-term differentiation of the solution (17.7) of Legendre's equation, we obtain the solution

$$Q_n^m(\mu) = (-1)^m \frac{\Gamma(\tfrac{1}{2})\Gamma(m+n+1)}{2^{n+1}\Gamma(n+\tfrac{3}{2})}\mu^{-m-n-1}(\mu^2-1)^{\frac{1}{2}m}$$

$$\times {}_2F_1\left(\tfrac{1}{2}m+\tfrac{1}{2}n+\tfrac{1}{2},\ \tfrac{1}{2}m+\tfrac{1}{2}n+1;\ n+\tfrac{3}{2};\ \frac{1}{\mu^2}\right) \quad (21.13)$$

of Legendre's associated equation.

Solutions of the type (21.7) and (21.8) can be derived in a similar fashion. Using the result

$$\int_1^\mu \int_1^\xi \cdots \int_1^\xi \left(\frac{1-\xi}{2}\right)^r (d\xi)^m = \frac{1}{m!}(\mu-1)^m \frac{r!}{(m+1)_r}\left(\frac{1-\mu}{2}\right)^r$$

in equation (21.7), with Murphy's expression (15.2) for $P_n(\mu)$, we derive the expression

$$\frac{1}{m!}(\mu-1)^m {}_2F_1\left(-n,\ n+1;\ m+1;\ \frac{1-\mu}{2}\right) \quad (21.14)$$

for

$$\int_1^\mu \int_1^\xi \cdots \int_1^\xi P_n(\xi)(d\xi)^m,$$

and this yields the solution

$$P_n^{-m}(\mu) = \frac{1}{m!}\left(\frac{\mu-1}{\mu+1}\right)^{\frac{1}{2}m} {}_2F_1\left(-n,\, n+1;\, m+1;\, \frac{1-\mu}{2}\right). \quad (21.15)$$

The solution provided by Rodrigues' formula (15.3) can obviously be written as

$$P_n^{-m}(\mu) = \frac{(\mu^2-1)^{-\frac{1}{2}m}}{2^n n!}\frac{d^{n-m}}{d\mu^{n-m}}(\mu^2-1)^n. \quad (21.16)$$

In a similar way the solution

$$Q_n^{-m}(\mu) = (-1)^m \frac{\Gamma(\frac{1}{2})\Gamma(n-m+1)}{2^{n+1}\Gamma(n+\frac{3}{2})}\cdot\frac{(\mu^2-1)^{-\frac{1}{2}m}}{\mu^{n-m+1}}$$

$$\times {}_2F_1\left(\tfrac{1}{2}n-\tfrac{1}{2}m+\tfrac{1}{2},\, \tfrac{1}{2}n-\tfrac{1}{2}m+1;\, n+\tfrac{3}{2};\, \frac{1}{\mu^2}\right) \quad (21.17)$$

is derived from equation (21.8) and the result

$$\Gamma(n+1)\int_\infty^\mu\int_\infty^\xi\cdots\int_\infty^\xi\frac{(\frac{1}{2}n+\frac{1}{2})_r(\frac{1}{2}n+1)_r}{\xi^{n+1+2r}}(d\xi)^m$$

$$= (-1)^m\Gamma(n-m+1)\frac{(\frac{1}{2}n-\frac{1}{2}m+\frac{1}{2})_r(\frac{1}{2}n-\frac{1}{2}m+1)_r}{\mu^{n-m+1+2r}}$$

used in equation (17.7).

The four functions $P_n^m(\mu)$, $Q_n^m(\mu)$, $P_n^{-m}(\mu)$, $Q_n^{-m}(\mu)$ defined equations (21.9), (21.13), (21.15) and (21.17) respectively are therefore solutions of Legendre's associated equation. They are known as **Legendre's associated functions.** Although the expressions above have been found by assuming m and n to be integers it is readily shown that the solutions quoted are valid even when m and n are not integers. Since Legendre's associated equation is of the second degree it follows that only two of these four functions are linearly independent, and that the other two may be expressed simply in terms of them. It follows immediately from equations (21.11) and (21.15) that if m, n are integers

$$P_n^{-m}(\mu) = \frac{\Gamma(n-m+1)}{\Gamma(n+m+1)} P_n^m(\mu). \qquad (21.18)$$

Furthermore, if we apply the result (7.6) to the hypergeometric series on the right-hand side of equation (21.17) we find that

$$Q_n^{-m}(\mu) = (-1)^m \frac{\Gamma(\tfrac{1}{2})\Gamma(n-m+1)}{2^{n+1}\Gamma(n+\tfrac{3}{2})} \mu^{-m-n-1}(\mu^2-1)^{\frac{1}{2}m}$$

$$\times {}_2F_1\left(\tfrac{1}{2}m+\tfrac{1}{2}n+\tfrac{1}{2},\ \tfrac{1}{2}m+\tfrac{1}{2}n+1;\ n+\tfrac{3}{2};\ \frac{1}{\mu^2}\right)$$

which, on comparison with equation (21.13), reveals the relation

$$Q_n^{-m}(\mu) = \frac{\Gamma(n-m+1)}{\Gamma(n+m+1)} Q_n^m(\mu). \qquad (21.19)$$

It is now a simple matter to prove that when m and n are integers, and m is fixed, the polynomials $P_n^m(\mu)$ form an orthogonal sequence for the interval $(-1, 1)$. Making use of the results (21.18), (21.12) and (21.16) we find that

$$\int_{-1}^{1} P_n^m(\mu)P_{n'}^m(\mu)d\mu = \frac{\Gamma(n+m+1)}{\Gamma(n-m+1)} \frac{1}{2^{n+n'}n!n'!}$$

$$\int_{-1}^{1} \frac{d^{n-m}}{d\mu^{n-m}}(\mu^2-1)^n \frac{d^{n'+m}}{d\mu^{n'+m}}(\mu^2-1)^{n'}d\mu$$

and after integrating by parts $n-m$ times the expression on the right reduces to

$$\frac{\Gamma(n+m+1)}{\Gamma(n-m+1)} \frac{(-1)^{n-m}}{2^{n+n'}n!n'!} \int_{-1}^{1}(\mu^2-1)^n \frac{d^{n+n'}}{d\mu^{n+n'}}(\mu^2-1)^{n'}d\mu.$$

This integral is evaluated by the method used at the end

of § 15 and we find that

$$\int_{-1}^{1} P_n^m(\mu)P_{n'}^m(\mu)d\mu = \frac{\Gamma(n+m+1)}{\Gamma(n-m+1)}(-1)^m \frac{2}{2n+1} \delta_{n,\,n'} \quad (21.20)$$

In many physical problems $\mu = \cos\theta$ so that $-1 \leqq \mu \leqq 1$. It is then not always convenient to have a factor of the form $(\mu^2-1)^{\frac{1}{2}m}$. We use instead **Ferrer's function**

$$T_n^m(\mu) = (1-\mu^2)^{\frac{1}{2}m} \frac{d^m P_n(\mu)}{d\mu^m}. \quad (21.21)$$

With this notation we may write (21.20) in the form

$$\int_{-1}^{1} T_n^m(\mu)T_{n'}^m(\mu)d\mu = \frac{\Gamma(n+m+1)}{\Gamma(n-m+1)} \frac{2}{2n+1} \delta_{n,\,n'}. \quad (21.22)$$

The other formulæ are amended similarly.

§ 22. Integral expression for the associated Legendre function.

If we assume Cauchy's theorem in the form †

$$\frac{1}{2\pi i} \int_C \frac{f(\zeta)}{\zeta-\mu} d\zeta = f(\mu)$$

where $f(\zeta)$ is an analytic function of the complex variable ζ in a certain domain R which includes the point $\zeta = \mu$ and where the integral is taken along a closed contour C which includes $\zeta = \mu$ and lies wholly within the domain R, then by differentiating both sides of the equation r times with respect to μ we obtain the result

$$\frac{d^r f(\mu)}{d\mu^r} = \frac{r!}{2\pi i} \int_C \frac{f(\zeta)}{(\zeta-\mu)^{r+1}} d\zeta. \quad (22.1)$$

Substituting $m+n$ for r and $(\zeta^2-1)^n$ for $f(\zeta)$ in this equation

† E. G. Phillips, *Functions of a Complex Variable* (Oliver and Boyd, 1940), p. 93.

we find that, as a result of equation (21.1),

$$P_n^m(\mu) = \frac{(m+n)!}{2^n \cdot n!} \frac{(\mu^2-1)^{\frac{1}{2}m}}{2\pi i} \int_C \frac{(\zeta^2-1)^n}{(\zeta-\mu)^{m+n+1}} \, d\zeta. \quad (22.2)$$

If $\mu > 0$ we may take the contour C to be the circle

$$|\zeta - \mu| = |\sqrt{(\mu^2-1)}|.$$

Integrating round this contour we obtain from equation (22.2) the equation

$$\frac{1}{2\pi} \int_0^{2\pi} \{\mu + \sqrt{(\mu^2-1)} \cos(\phi-\psi)\}^n \frac{\cos}{\sin} (m\phi) d\phi$$

$$= \frac{n!}{(n+m)!} \frac{\cos}{\sin} (m\psi) P_n^m(\mu)$$

from which follows immediately the Fourier expansion

$$\{\mu + \sqrt{(\mu^2-1)} \cos(\phi-\psi)\}^n$$

$$= P_n(\mu) + 2 \sum_{m=1}^n \frac{n!}{(n+m)!} P_n^m(\mu) \cos m(\psi-\phi). \quad (22.3)$$

Changing n to $-(n+1)$ we obtain the expansion

$$\{\mu' + \sqrt{(\mu'^2-1)} \cos \psi\}^{-n-1}$$

$$= P_n(\mu') + 2 \sum_{m=1}^n (-1)^m \frac{(n-m)!}{n!} P_n^m(\mu') \cos m\psi. \quad (22.4)$$

. Applying Parseval's theorem for Fourier series to the series (22.3) and (22.4) we find that the series

$$P_n(\mu)P_n(\mu') + 2 \sum_{m=1}^n (-1)^m \frac{(n-m)!}{(n+m)!} P_n^m(\mu) P_n^m(\mu') \cos m\phi$$

converges to the sum

$$\frac{1}{2\pi} \int_{-\pi}^{\pi} \frac{\{\mu + \sqrt{(\mu^2-1)} \cos(\psi+\phi)\}^n}{\{\mu' + \sqrt{(\mu'^2-1)} \cos \psi\}^{n+1}} \, d\psi.$$

This integral may be evaluated by means of Cauchy's theorem.† Its value is found to be

$$P_n\{\mu\mu' + \sqrt{[(\mu^2-1)(\mu'^2-1)]}\cos\phi)\}.$$

Writing $\mu = \cos\theta$, $\mu' = \cos\theta'$ and

$$\cos\Theta = \cos\theta\cos\theta' + \sin\theta\sin\theta'\cos\phi$$

we obtain the result

$$P_n(\cos\Theta) = P_n(\cos\theta)P_n(\cos\theta')$$

$$+2\sum_{m=1}^{n}(-1)^m\frac{(n-m)!}{(n+m)!}P_n^m(\cos\theta)P_n^m(\cos\theta),\cos(m\phi) \quad (22.5)$$

which is often of value in the solution of problems in wave mechanics.

§ **23. Surface spherical harmonics.** From the two sets of orthogonal functions $T_n^m(\cos\theta)$, $\cos(m\phi)$ we can form a third set of functions

$$X_{n,\,m}(\theta,\,\phi)$$
$$= \left(\frac{2n+1}{2\pi}\right)^{\frac{1}{2}}\left\{\frac{(n-m)!}{(n+m)!}\right\}^{\frac{1}{2}}T_n^m(\cos\theta)\cos m\phi, \quad (m\leqq n) \quad (23.1)$$

which is an orthogonal set of functions on the unit sphere, i.e. the functions of the set satisfy the normalisation relation

$$\int_0^\pi\sin\theta\,d\theta\int_0^{2\pi}X_{n,\,m}X_{n',\,m'}d\phi = \delta_{nn'}\delta_{mm'}. \quad (23.2)$$

In a similar way we can construct a set

$$Y_{n,\,m}(\theta,\,\phi) = \left(\frac{2n+1}{2\pi}\right)^{\frac{1}{2}}\left\{\frac{(n-m)!}{(n+m)!}\right\}^{\frac{1}{2}}T_n^m(\cos\theta)\sin m\phi,$$
$$(m\leqq n) \quad (23.3)$$

† For details, see E. W. Hobson, *op. cit.*, pp. 365-71.

which satisfies the relations

$$\int_0^\pi \sin\theta\,d\theta \int_0^{2\pi} Y_{n,\,m}Y_{n',\,m'}\,d\phi = \delta_{nn'}\delta_{mm'}, \tag{23.4}$$

$$\int_0^\pi \sin\theta\,d\theta \int_0^{2\pi} X_{n,\,m}Y_{n',\,m'}\,d\phi = 0 \tag{23.5}$$

for all integral values of n, n', m and m' with $m \leqq n$, $m' \leqq n'$.

Because of these orthogonality relationships we can establish an expansion theorem which is a straightforward generalisation of the Legendre series (16.3). It is readily shown that for a large class of functions f, the function $f(\theta, \phi)$ can be represented by the series

$$\sum_{n=0}^\infty c_n P_n(\cos\theta)$$
$$+ \sum_{n=1}^\infty \sum_{m=1}^\infty \{x_{nm}X_{n,\,m}(\theta,\,\phi) + y_{nm}Y_{n,\,m}(\theta,\,\phi)\} \tag{23.6}$$

where the coefficients c_n, x_{nm}, y_{nm} are given by the expressions

$$c_n = \frac{2n+1}{4\pi} \int_0^{2\pi} d\phi \int_0^\pi f(\theta,\,\phi) P_n(\cos\theta) \sin\theta\,d\theta, \tag{23.7}$$

$$x_{nm} = \int_0^\pi \sin\theta\,d\theta \int_0^{2\pi} X_{n,\,m}(\theta,\,\phi) f(\theta,\,\phi)\,d\phi, \tag{23.8}$$

$$y_{nm} = \int_0^\pi \sin\theta\,d\theta \int_0^{2\pi} Y_{n,\,m}(\theta,\,\phi) f(\theta,\,\phi)\,d\phi. \tag{23.9}$$

For any given function $f(\theta, \phi)$ the series (23.6) can therefore in principle be computed by a series of simple integrations.

The functions $X_{n,\,m}$ and $Y_{n,\,m}$, which are known as **surface spherical harmonics,** can be constructed easily from the known expressions for the associated functions T_n^m. We find, for instance, that

$$X_{1,\,1}(\theta,\,\phi) = -\left(\frac{3}{4\pi}\right)^{\frac{1}{2}} \sin\theta\cos\phi,$$

$$X_{2,\,1}(\theta,\,\phi) = -\left(\frac{15}{4\pi}\right)^{\frac{1}{2}} \sin\theta\cos\theta\cos\phi,$$

$$X_{2,\,2}(\theta,\,\phi) = \left(\frac{15}{16\pi}\right)^{\frac{1}{2}} \sin^2\theta\cos 2\phi,$$

$$X_{3,\,1}(\theta,\,\phi) = -\left(\frac{21}{32\pi}\right)^{\frac{1}{2}} \sin\theta(5\cos^2\theta-1)\cos\phi,$$

$$X_{3,\,2}(\theta,\,\phi) = \left(\frac{105}{16\pi}\right)^{\frac{1}{2}} \sin^2\theta\cos\theta\cos 2\phi,$$

$$X_{3,\,3}(\theta,\,\phi) = -\left(\frac{35}{32\pi}\right)^{\frac{1}{2}} \sin^3\theta\cos 3\phi,$$

and the corresponding expressions for the $Y_{n,\,m}$ are obtained by replacing $\cos(m\phi)$ by $\sin(m\phi)$ in the expressions for the $X_{n,\,m}$.

The functions $X_{n,\,m}$ and $Y_{n,\,m}$ have the important property that they are solutions of the partial differential equation

$$\frac{1}{\sin\theta}\frac{\partial}{\partial\theta}\left(\sin\theta\frac{\partial X}{\partial\theta}\right) + \frac{1}{\sin^2\theta}\frac{\partial^2 X}{\partial\phi^2} + n(n+1)X = 0 \quad (23.10)$$

so that the function

$$(Ar^n + Br^{-n-1})X_{n,\,m}(\theta,\,\phi) + (Cr^n + Dr^{-n-1})Y_{n,\,m}(\theta,\,\phi),$$

where A, B, C and D are constants, is a solution of Laplace's equation. It follows immediately from equations (23.7)-(23.9) taken with the expansion (23.6) that the function

$$\psi(r,\,\theta,\,\phi) = \sum_{n=0}^{\infty} c_n\left(\frac{r}{a}\right)^n P_n(\cos\theta)$$

$$+ \sum_{n=1}^{\infty}\sum_{m=1}^{\infty}\left(\frac{r}{a}\right)^n\{x_{nm}X_{n,\,m}(\theta,\,\phi) + y_{nm}Y_{n,\,m}(\theta,\,\phi)\}$$

G

satisfies Laplace's equation in the region $0 \leq r \leq a$, is finite at $r = 0$, and takes the value $f(\theta, \phi)$ on the sphere $r = a$.

For example, suppose we wish to find the solution of Laplace's equation which takes on the value x^2 on the surface of the sphere $r = a$. Here we have

$$f(\theta, \phi) = a^2 \sin^2 \theta \cos^2 \phi$$

$$= \frac{a^2}{3} - \frac{a^2}{3} \left(\frac{3 \cos^2 \theta - 1}{2} \right) + \tfrac{1}{2} a^2 \sin^2 \theta \cos 2\phi$$

$$= \frac{a^2}{3} - \frac{a^2}{3} P_2(\cos \theta) + \left(\frac{4\pi}{15} \right)^{\frac{1}{2}} X_{2, 2}(\theta, \phi) a^2.$$

Thus the required solution is

$$\psi(r, \theta, \phi) = \frac{1}{3} a^2 - \frac{1}{3} r^2 P_2(\cos \theta) + \left(\frac{4}{15} \right)^{\frac{1}{2}} r^2 X_{2, 2}(\theta, \phi).$$

Substituting the values of P_2 and $X_{2, 2}$ and transforming back to Cartesian coordinates we see that the required solution is

$$\psi = \tfrac{1}{3}(a^2 + 2x^2 - y^2 - z^2).$$

§ 24. Use of associated Legendre functions in wave mechanics.

To illustrate the use of associated Legendre functions in wave mechanics, we shall consider one of the simplest problems in that subject—that of solving Schrödinger's equation

$$\nabla^2 \psi + \frac{8\pi^2 m}{h^2} (W - V)\psi = 0 \qquad (24.1)$$

for the rotator with free axis, that is for a particle moving on the surface of a sphere. In equation (24.1), W represents the total energy of the system, V the potential energy. In the case under consideration V is a constant, V_0 say, and the wave function ψ will be a function of θ, ϕ only. If the radius of the sphere is denoted by a then equation

(24.1) is of the form

$$\frac{1}{a^2}\frac{\partial^2\psi}{\partial\theta^2} + \frac{\cot\theta}{a^2}\frac{\partial\psi}{\partial\theta} + \frac{1}{a^2\sin\theta}\frac{\partial^2\psi}{\partial\phi^2} + \frac{8\pi^2 m(W-V_0)}{h^2}\,\psi = 0.$$

(24.2)

If we consider solutions of the form

$$\psi = \Theta e^{\pm im\phi}$$

then

$$\Theta'' + \Theta'\cot\theta + \frac{8\pi^2 ma^2(W-V_0)}{h^2}\,\Theta - \frac{m^2}{\sin^2\theta}\,\Theta = 0.$$

Substituting

$$\mu = \cos\theta, \quad \frac{8\pi^2 ma^2(W-V_0)}{h^2} = n(n+1) \qquad (24.3)$$

we find that this equation reduces to Legendre's associated equation (21.1) and hence has solution

$$\Theta = AP_n^m(\cos\theta) + BQ_n^m(\cos\theta).$$

However, for the same reason as in the case of potential theory (§ 20 above), we must take $B = 0$. The solutions of equation (24.2) will therefore be made up of combinations of solutions of the form

$$\psi_{m,\,n}(\theta,\,\phi) = A_{mn}e^{\pm im\phi}P_n^m(\cos\theta), \qquad (24.4)$$

where A_{mn} is a constant.

The physical conditions imposed on the wave function ψ are that it should be single-valued and continuous. Obviously then the "physical" solutions will have m an integer, since $\psi_{m,\,n}(\theta,\,\phi+2\pi)$ must equal $\psi_{m,\,n}(\theta,\,\phi)$. Further, in order that the series for $P_n^m(\mu)$ should converge for the values $\mu = \pm 1$ it is necessary that it should have only a finite number of terms. This is possible only if n is a positive integer. If therefore the solution (24.4) is to be valid for $\theta = 0$ and $\theta = \pi$ we must have n a positive integer. The physical conditions on the wave function are therefore not satisfied by systems with an arbitrary value for the energy W but only by systems for which

$$W = V_0 + \frac{h^2}{8\pi^2 ma^2} n(n+1), \qquad (24.5)$$

where n is a positive integer. In other words, the energy of such a mechanical system does not vary continuously, but is capable of assuming values taken from the discrete set (24.5).

Examples III

(1) Show that, if n is odd $P_n(0) = 0$, and that, if n is even,

$$P_n(0) = \frac{(-1)^{\frac{1}{2}n}(\frac{1}{2})_{\frac{1}{2}n}}{(\frac{1}{2}n)!} = \frac{(-1)^{\frac{1}{2}n}n!}{2^n\{(\frac{1}{2}n)!\}^2}.$$

(2) Prove that

$$\sum_{n=0}^{\infty} \frac{\mu^{n+1}}{n+1} P_n(\mu) = \frac{1}{2} \log\left\{\frac{1+\mu}{1-\mu}\right\}.$$

(3) If $\zeta = \mu + \sqrt{(\mu^2 - 1)}$ show that

(i) $(1-h\zeta)^{-\frac{1}{2}}(1-h/\zeta)^{-\frac{1}{2}} = \sum_{n=0}^{\infty} h^n P_n(\mu)$;

(ii) $P_n(\mu) = \frac{\Gamma(n+\frac{1}{2})}{n!\Gamma(\frac{1}{2})} \zeta^n {}_2F_1(\frac{1}{2}, -n; \frac{1}{2}-n; \zeta^{-2})$.

Deduce that

(iii) ${}_2F_1(\frac{1}{2}, -n; \frac{1}{2}-n; 1) = \frac{n!\Gamma(\frac{1}{2})}{\Gamma(n+\frac{1}{2})}$.

(4) If n is a positive integer prove that

$$\int_{-1}^{1} P_n(\mu)(1-2\mu h+h^2)^{-\frac{1}{2}}d\mu = \frac{2h^n}{2n+1},$$

and hence, making use of Rodrigues' formula, deduce that

$$\int_{-1}^{1} (1-\mu^2)^n (1-2\mu h+h^2)^{-n-\frac{1}{2}} d\mu = \frac{2^{2n+1}(n!)^2}{(2n+1)!}.$$

(5) Prove that

$$P_n'(x) = \sum_{r=0}^{p} (2n-4r-1)P_{n-2r-1}(x),$$

where $p = \frac{1}{2}(n-1)$ or $\frac{1}{2}n-1$ according as n is odd or even.

Deduce that for all x in the closed interval $(-1, 1)$ and for all positive integers n, the values of the functions

$$|P_n(x)|, \quad n^{-2}|P_n'(x)|, \quad n^{-4}|P''(x)|, \quad \dots$$

can never exceed unity.

(6) Prove that

$$\int_{\mu}^{1} P_n(\mu)d\mu = \frac{1}{2n+1}\{P_{n-1}(\mu)-P_{n+1}(\mu)\},$$

and deduce, from example 1, that if n is an odd integer

$$\int_{0}^{1} P_n(\mu)d\mu = \frac{(-1)^{\frac{1}{2}n-\frac{1}{2}}(n-1)!}{2^n(\frac{1}{2}n+\frac{1}{2})!(\frac{1}{2}n-\frac{1}{2})!}.$$

What is the value of the integral when n is even?

(7) Using equation (14.2) and the results of the last example show that, if n is even,

$$\int_{0}^{1} \mu P_n(\mu)d\mu = (-1)^{\frac{1}{2}n-1}\frac{(n-2)!}{2^n(\frac{1}{2}n+1)!(\frac{1}{2}n-1)!},$$

and that the integral has the value zero if n is odd.

(8) If

$$u_n = \int_{-1}^{1} P_n(\mu)P_{n-1}(\mu)\frac{d\mu}{\mu},$$

prove that $(n+1)u_{n+1}+nu_n = 2$. Hence evaluate u_n.

(9) If m and n are positive integers, prove that

$$\int_{-1}^{1} (1+\mu)^{m+n} P_n(\mu)d\mu = \frac{2^{m+n+1}\{(m+n)!\}^2}{m!(m+2n+1)!}.$$

(10) If n is even and $m > -1$, prove that

$$\int_{0}^{1} \mu^m P_n(\mu)d\mu = \frac{\Gamma(\frac{1}{2}m+\frac{1}{2})\Gamma(\frac{1}{2}m+1)}{2\Gamma(\frac{1}{2}m+\frac{1}{2}n+\frac{3}{2})\Gamma(\frac{1}{2}m-\frac{1}{2}n+1)}.$$

Deduce that

$$\int_{0}^{1} (1-k\mu^2)^{-n-\frac{3}{2}} P_{2n}(\mu)d\mu = \frac{1}{2n+1} k^n(1-k)^{-n-\frac{1}{2}}.$$

(11) Show that

$$P_n(\mu) = \left(\frac{\mu+1}{2}\right)^n {}_2F_1\left(-n; -n, 1; \frac{\mu-1}{\mu+1}\right),$$

and hence that

$$(1-t)^n P_n\left(\frac{1+t}{1-t}\right) = \sum_{r=0}^{n} ({}^nC_r)^2 t^r.$$

Deduce that

$$P_n(\cosh u) \geqq 1.$$

(12) If $f(\mu) = (\mu^2-1)^n$ show, by using Rolle's theorem, that $f'(\mu)$ must have at least one zero between -1 and 1. Proceeding in this way deduce that $f^{(n)}(\mu)$ has n zeros between -1 and 1.

Hence show that when n is even the zeros of $P_n(\mu)$ occur in pairs, equal in magnitude but opposite in sign, and that when n is odd, $\mu = 0$ is a zero and the others occur in equal and opposite pairs.

(13) If $y(\mu)$ is any solution of the linear differential equation

$$\alpha(\mu)\frac{d^2y}{d\mu^2} + \beta(\mu)\frac{dy}{d\mu} + \gamma(\mu)y = 0$$

in which α, β and γ are continuous functions of μ whose derivatives of all orders are continuous, prove that $y(\mu)$ cannot have any repeated zeros except possibly for values of μ which satisfy the equation $\alpha(\mu) = 0$.

Deduce that all the zeros of $P_n(\mu)$ are distinct.

(14) Prove that the Legendre polynomial $P_n(x)$ has the smallest distance in the mean from zero of all polynomials of degree n with leading coefficient $2^n(\tfrac{1}{2})_n/n!$

(15) If R denotes the operator

$$\frac{d}{dx}\left\{(1-x^2)\,\frac{d}{dx}\right\},$$

prove that

$$\int_{-1}^{1} P_n(x)R\{f(x)\}dx = -n(n+1)\int_{-1}^{1} P_n(x)f(x)dx$$

provided that $f(x)$ and $f'(x)$ are finite at $x = \pm 1$.

Prove that if $n \geq 1$

$$\int_{-1}^{1} \log(1-x)P_n(x)dx = -\frac{2}{n(n+1)}.$$

(16) Prove that

(i) $\displaystyle\int_{-1}^{1} \frac{P_n(x)dx}{\sqrt{(1-x)}} = \frac{2\sqrt{2}}{2n+1}$;

(ii) $\displaystyle\int_{-1}^{1} \frac{P_n(x)dx}{(1-2hx+h^2)^{\frac{3}{2}}} = \frac{2h^n}{1-h^2}.$

(17) If $R^2 = 1-2hx+h^2$, prove that if $|h|<1$, $n \geq 1$,

(i) $\displaystyle\int_{-1}^{1} \log\left\{\frac{h-x+R}{1-x}\right\} P_n(x)dx = \frac{2h^{n+1}}{(2n+1)(n+1)}$;

(ii) $\displaystyle\int_{-1}^{1} \log(1-hx+R)P_n(x)dx = -\frac{2h^n}{n(2n+1)}.$

(18) If
$$f(x, a) = \int_0^a \frac{\xi^{m-1}}{(1-2\xi x+\xi^2)^{\frac{1}{2}}}\, d\xi, \quad (m>1),$$

prove that
$$\int_{-1}^1 f(x, a)P_n(x)dx = \frac{2a^{n+m}}{(n+m)(2n+1)}.$$

(19) If z is real and $|z|<1$ prove that
$$\int_0^\pi \frac{d\phi}{1+z\cos\phi} = \frac{\pi}{\sqrt{(1-z^2)}}.$$

Putting $z = \mp h\sqrt{(\mu^2-1)}/(1-h\mu)$ where h is so small that
$$|h\{\mu\pm\sqrt{(\mu^2-1)}\cos\phi\}|<1$$

$(0\leq\phi\leq\pi)$, expanding both sides in powers of h, and equating coefficients of h^n show that
$$P_n(\mu) = \frac{1}{\pi}\int_0^\pi \{\mu\pm\sqrt{(\mu^2-1)}\cos\phi\}^n d\phi.$$

Hence evaluate the sum
$$\sum_{r=0}^n {}^nC_r P_r(\cos\theta).$$

(20) Show by making the substitution
$$z = \pm h\sqrt{(\mu^2-1)}/(h\mu-1)$$

in the formula in ex. 19 that
$$P_n(\mu) = \frac{1}{\pi}\int_0^\pi \frac{d\phi}{\{\mu+\sqrt{(\mu^2-1)}\cos\phi\}^{n+1}}.$$

(21) Making use of the integral expression for $P_n(\mu)$ derived in ex. 19 show that
$$P_n(\mu) = \sum_{r=0}^n {}^nC_r(1-\mu^2)^{\frac{1}{2}n-\frac{1}{2}r}\mu^r P_{n-r}(0).$$

Deduce that

$$\begin{vmatrix} P_0(\mu) & P_1(\mu) & P_2(\mu) \\ P_1(\mu) & P_2(\mu) & P_3(\mu) \\ P_2(\mu) & P_3(\mu) & P_4(\mu) \end{vmatrix} = (1-\mu^2)^3 \begin{vmatrix} P_0(0) & 0 & P_2(0) \\ 0 & P_2(0) & 0 \\ P_2(0) & 0 & P_4(0) \end{vmatrix}.$$

(22) Prove that if $\mu > 1$

$$Q_n(\mu) = \frac{1}{2^{n+1}} \int_{-1}^{1} \frac{(1-t^2)^n}{(\mu-t)^{n+1}} \, dt,$$

and deduce that

$$Q_n(\mu) = \int_0^\alpha \{\mu - \sqrt{(\mu^2-1)} \cosh \theta\}^n \, d\theta,$$

where $\alpha = \frac{1}{2} \log (\mu+1)/(\mu-1)$.

Hence find expressions for $Q_0(\mu)$ and $Q_1(\mu)$.

(23) Determine the simple expressions for $Q_0(\mu)$, $Q_1(\mu)$, $Q_2(\mu)$ and $Q_3(\mu)$ by working out the values of the polynomial $W_{n-1}(\mu)$, occurring in equation (18.8), for these values of n.

(24) Establish the following formulæ due to MacRobert:

(i) $\mu P_m(\mu) Q_n(\mu) = \frac{1}{2} \int_{-1}^{1} \frac{\xi P_m(\xi) P_n(\xi)}{\mu - \xi} \, d\xi, \quad m < n;$

(ii) $\mu P_n(\mu) Q_n(\mu) = \frac{1}{2} \int_{-1}^{1} \frac{\xi \{P_n(\xi)\}^2}{\mu - \xi} \, d\xi + \frac{1}{2n+1};$

(iii) $\mu^m(\mu^2-1) Q_n'(\mu) = \frac{1}{2} \int_{-1}^{1} \frac{\xi^m(\xi^2-1) P_n'(\xi)}{\mu - \xi} \, d\xi, \quad n > m;$

(iv) $(\mu^2-1) P_m(\mu) Q_n'(\mu) = \frac{1}{2} \int_{-1}^{1} \frac{(\xi^2-1) P_m(\xi) P_n'(\xi)}{\mu - \xi} \, d\xi, \quad n > m.$

(25) Prove that, if n is a positive integer and $\zeta = \mu + \sqrt{(\mu^2-1)}$,

$$Q_n(\mu) = \zeta \int_0^\pi \frac{P_n(\cos \theta) \sin \theta \, d\theta}{1 - 2\zeta \cos \theta + \zeta^2}.$$

Deduce that, if $|\zeta| > 1$,

$$Q_n(\mu) = \sum_{m=1}^{\infty} \zeta^{-m} \int_0^{\pi} P_n(\cos\theta) \sin m\theta \, d\theta.$$

By evaluating this integral show that

$$Q_n(\mu) = \frac{\sqrt{\pi} n!}{\Gamma(n+\frac{3}{2})} \zeta^{-n-1} \, {}_2F_1(\tfrac{1}{2}, n+1; n+\tfrac{3}{2}; \zeta^{-2}).$$

(26) Prove that, if m is a positive integer,

$$\sum_{n=m}^{\infty} h^{n-m} T_n^m(\mu) = \frac{(-1)^m (2m)! (1-\mu^2)^{\frac{1}{2}m}}{2^m m! (1-2\mu h + h^2)^{m+\frac{1}{2}}}.$$

(27) Show that, if $|\mu| > 1$, $n > -1$ then

$$Q_n^m(\mu) = \frac{\Gamma(n+m+1)}{\Gamma(n+1)} \frac{(\mu^2-1)^{\frac{1}{2}m}}{2^{n+1}} \int_{-1}^{1} \frac{(1-\xi^2)^n d\xi}{(\mu-\xi)^{n+m+1}}.$$

Deduce that, if $|\mu+1| > 2$ then

$$Q_n^m(\mu) = \frac{\sqrt{\pi}\Gamma(n+m+1)}{2^{n-1}\Gamma(n+\frac{3}{2})} \frac{(\mu^2-1)^{\frac{1}{2}m}}{(\mu+1)^{n+m+1}}$$
$$\qquad\qquad {}_2F_1\left(n+2, n+m+1; 2n+2; \frac{2}{\mu+1}\right).$$

Find a simple expression for $Q_n^{n+1}(\mu)$.

(28) Prove the following recurrence relations for Ferrer's Associated Legendre Functions:

(i) $T_{n+1}^{m+1}(\mu) - T_{n-1}^{m+1}(\mu) = (2n+1)(1-\mu^2)^{\frac{1}{2}} T_n^m(\mu)$;

(ii) $(n-m+1)T_{n+1}^m(\mu) - (2n+1)\mu T_n^m(\mu)$
$$\qquad\qquad\qquad + (n+m)T_{n-1}^m(\mu) = 0;$$

(iii) $T_n^{m+1}(\mu) - T_{n-1}^{m+1}(\mu) = (n-m)(1-\mu^2)^{\frac{1}{2}} T_n^m(\mu)$.

(29) Derive the expressions for $T_4^m(\theta, \phi)$ and $X_4^m(\theta, \phi)$

for $m = 1, 2, 3, 4$. Express the functions $\sin^2 \theta \sin^2 \phi$, $\sin^2 \theta \cos^2 \phi$, $\sin \theta \cos^3 \theta \cos \phi$ in terms of surface spherical harmonics.

(30) Find the function which satisfies Laplace's equation in the interior of the sphere $x^2 + y^2 + z^2 = a^2$, remains finite at the origin and takes the value $\alpha x^2 + \beta y^2 + \gamma z^2$ on the surface of the sphere.

(31) The *Jacobi polynomials* are defined by the equation †

$$\mathscr{F}_m(a, b, x) = {}_2F_1(-m, a+m; b; x).$$

If $D \equiv d/dx$ show that

$$D^m\{x^{b+m-1}(1-x)^{a+m-b}\} = (b)_m x^{b-1} {}_2F_1(b-a-m, b+m; b; x)$$

Deduce that

(i) $\mathscr{F}_m(a, b, x) = \dfrac{x^{1-b}(1-x)^{b-a}}{(b)_m} D^m\{x^{b+m-1}(1-x)^{a+m-b}\};$

(ii) $\displaystyle\int_0^1 x^{b-1}(1-x)^{a-b} f(x)\mathscr{F}_m(a, b, x)dx$

$$= \frac{1}{(b)_m} \int_0^1 (-1)^m f^{(m)}(x) x^{b+m-1}(1-x)^{a+m-b}dx;$$

(iii) $\displaystyle\int_0^1 x^{b-1}(1-x)^{a-b}\mathscr{F}_m(a, b, x)\mathscr{F}_n(a, b, x)dx = 0, \quad m \neq n;$

(iv) $\displaystyle\int_0^1 x^{b-1}(1-x)^{a-b}\{\mathscr{F}_m(a, b, x)\}^2$

$$= \frac{\Gamma(b)\Gamma(a+1-b)(a+1-b)_m}{\Gamma(a)(a)_m(b)_m} \times \frac{m!}{a+2m}$$

(32) The *Tchebichef polynomials* of the first and second

---

† It should be observed that this name is sometimes applied to the polynomial

$$P_n^{(\alpha, \beta)}(x) = \frac{(a+1)_n}{n!} \mathscr{F}_n(\alpha+\beta+1, \alpha+1, \tfrac{1}{2}-\tfrac{1}{2}x).$$

kinds may be defined by the equations

$$T_n(x) = {}_2F_1\left(-n,\, n;\, \tfrac{1}{2};\, \frac{1-x}{2}\right),$$

$$U_n(x) = (n+1)\,{}_2F_1\left(-n,\, n+1;\, \tfrac{3}{2};\, \frac{1-x}{2}\right)$$

respectively.

From (2) on p. 43 show that

$$T_n(\cos\theta) = \cos n\theta, \quad U_n(\cos\theta) = \frac{\sin(n+1)\theta}{\sin\theta}.$$

Prove also that

(i) $1 + 2\sum\limits_{n=1}^{\infty} T_n(x)t^n = (1-t^2)(1-2tx+x^2)^{-1},$

$$|t| < 1, \quad |x| < 1;$$

(ii) $2^n(\tfrac{1}{2})_n T_n(x) = (-1)^n(1-x^2)^{\frac{1}{2}n}\,\dfrac{d^n}{dx^n}\,(1-x^2)^{n-\frac{1}{2}};$

(iii) $\displaystyle\int_{-1}^{1} T_m(x)T_n(x)(1-x^2)^{-\frac{1}{2}}dx = \tfrac{1}{2}\pi\delta_{mn};$

(iv) $\displaystyle\sum_{n=0}^{\infty} U_n(x)t^n = (1-2xt+t^2)^{-1};$

(v) $2^{n+1}(\tfrac{1}{2})_{n+1} U_n(x)$

$$= (-1)^n(n+1)(1-x^2)^{-\frac{1}{2}}\,\frac{d^n}{dx^n}\,(1-x^2)^{n+2};$$

(vi) $\displaystyle\int_{-1}^{1} U_m(x)U_n(x)(1-x^2)^{\frac{1}{2}}dx = \tfrac{1}{2}\pi\delta_{mn};$

(vii) $T_n(x) = U_m(x) - xU_{n-1}(x);$

(viii) $(1-x^2)U_{n-1}(x) = xT_n(x) - T_{n+1}(x).$

(33) The function $C_n^\nu(x)$ defined by

$$(1-2xt+t^2)^{-\nu} = \sum_{n=0}^{\infty} C_n^\nu(x)t^n \quad (\nu > 0)$$

is called the *Gegenbauer polynomial* of degree n and order ν.

Prove the relations:

(i) $C_n^v(x) = \dfrac{\Gamma(n+2v)}{n!\Gamma(2v)} \, _2F_1\left(n+2v, \; -n; \; v+\tfrac{1}{2}; \; \dfrac{1-x}{2}\right);$

(ii) $C_n^v(1) = (-1)^n c_n^v(-1) = \dfrac{\Gamma(n+2v)}{n!\Gamma(2v)};$

(iii) $C_n^v(x) = (-2)^n$

$$\dfrac{\Gamma(v+n)\Gamma(2v+n)}{n!\Gamma(v)\Gamma(2v+2n)} (1-x^2)^{\frac{1}{2}-v} \dfrac{d^n}{dx^n} (1-x^2)^{n+v-\frac{1}{2}};$$

(iv) $\displaystyle\int_{-1}^{1} C_n^v(x)C_m^v(x)(1-x^2)^{v-\frac{1}{2}}dx = \dfrac{2^{1-2v}\pi\Gamma(n+2v)}{n!(v+n)[\Gamma(v)]^2} \delta_{mn}.$

CHAPTER IV

BESSEL FUNCTIONS

§ **25. The origin of Bessel functions.** Bessel functions
were first introduced by Bessel, in 1824, in the discussion
of a problem in dynamical astronomy, which may be
described as follows. If P is a planet moving in an ellipse
whose focus S is the sun and whose centre and major axis
are C and $A'A$ respectively (cf. Fig. 8), then the angle

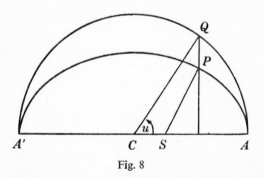

Fig. 8

ASP is called the *true anomaly* of the planet. It is found
that, in astronomical calculations, the true anomaly is
not a very convenient angle with which to deal. Instead we
use the *mean anomaly* ζ, which is defined to be 2π times
the ratio of the area of the elliptic sector ASP to the
area of the ellipse. Another angle of significance is the
eccentric anomaly, u, of the planet defined to be the angle
ACQ where Q is the point in which the ordinate through
P meets the auxiliary circle of the ellipse.

It is readily shown † by a simple geometrical argument that, if e is the eccentricity of the ellipse, the relation between the mean anomaly and the eccentric anomaly is

$$\zeta = u - e \sin u. \tag{25.1}$$

The problem set by Bessel was that of expressing the difference between the mean and eccentric anomalies, $u - \zeta$, as a series of sines of multiples of the mean anomaly, i.e. that of determining the coefficients $c_r (r = 1, 2, 3, \ldots)$ such that

$$u - \zeta = \sum_{r=1}^{\infty} c_r \sin (r\zeta). \tag{25.2}$$

To obtain the values of the coefficients c_r we multiply both sides of equation (25.2) by $\sin (s\zeta)$ and integrate with respect to ζ from 0 to π. We then obtain

$$\int_0^\pi (u - \zeta) \sin (s\zeta) d\zeta = \sum_{r=1}^{\infty} c_r \int_0^\pi \sin (r\zeta) \sin (s\zeta) d\zeta.$$

Now

$$\int_0^\pi \sin (r\zeta) \sin (s\zeta) d\zeta = \tfrac{1}{2}\pi \delta_{r,s}$$

and an integration by parts shows that

$$\int_0^\pi (u - \zeta) \sin (s\zeta) d\zeta$$
$$= \frac{1}{s}\left[(\zeta - u) \cos (s\zeta) \right]_0^\pi + \frac{1}{s} \int_0^\pi \left(\frac{du}{d\zeta} - 1 \right) \cos (s\zeta) d\zeta.$$

From (25.2), $\zeta - u$ is zero when $\zeta = 0$ and when $\zeta = \pi$, so that the square bracket vanishes; the integral can be written in the form

$$\frac{1}{s} \int_0^\pi \cos s\zeta \, du$$

† Cf. D. E. Rutherford, *Classical Mechanics* (Oliver and Boyd, 1951), § 42.

and hence, using equation (25.1) we obtain the result

$$c_s = \frac{2}{\pi s} \int_0^\pi \cos\{s(u - e \sin u)\} du. \qquad (25.3)$$

The integral on the right-hand side of equation (25.3) is a function of s and of the eccentricity e of the planet's orbit. If we write

$$J_n(x) = \frac{1}{\pi} \int_0^\pi \cos(x \sin \theta - n\theta) d\theta \qquad (25.4)$$

it follows from equations (25.3) and (25.2) that

$$u - \zeta = 2 \sum_{r=1}^\infty J_r(er) \frac{\sin(r\zeta)}{r}. \qquad (25.5)$$

The function $J_n(x)$ so defined is called **Bessel's coefficient of order n.**

We shall now show that $J_n(x)$ is equal to the coefficient of t^n in the expansion of $\exp\{\frac{1}{2}x(t - t^{-1})\}$; in other words we may define $J_n(x)$ by means of the expansion

$$\exp\left\{\frac{1}{2}x\left(t - \frac{1}{t}\right)\right\} = \sum_{n=-\infty}^\infty J_n(x)t^n. \qquad (25.6)$$

To prove this we need only show that the $J_n(x)$ of (25.6) can be expressed in the form (25.4). We first of all observe that

$$\sum_{n=-\infty}^\infty (-1)^n J_{-n}(x)t^n = \sum_{n=-\infty}^\infty J_n(x)\left(-\frac{1}{t}\right)^n = \sum_{n=-\infty}^\infty J_n(x)t^n$$

since both expansions are equal to $\exp\{\frac{1}{2}x(t - 1/t)\}$. Equating coefficients of t^n we have

$$(-1)^n J_{-n}(x) = J_n(x). \qquad (25.7)$$

In the expansion (25.6) we may write $t = e^{i\theta}$ to obtain the relation

$$\exp(ix\sin\theta) = \sum_{n=-\infty}^{\infty} J_n(x)e^{in\theta}.$$

Making use of the result (25.7) we see that the series on the right can be put into the form

$$J_0(x)+2\sum_{m=1}^{\infty} J_{2m}(x)\cos(2m\theta)+2i\sum_{m=1}^{\infty} J_{2m+1}(x)\sin(2m+1)\theta$$

so that by equating real and imaginary parts we obtain the expansions

$$\cos(x\sin\theta) = J_0(x)+2\sum_{m=1}^{\infty} J_{2m}(x)\cos(2m\theta), \quad (25.8)$$

$$\sin(x\sin\theta) = 2\sum_{m=0}^{\infty} J_{2m+1}(x)\sin(2m+1)\theta. \quad (25.9)$$

If we now multiply (25.8) by $\cos n\theta$, (25.9) by $\sin n\theta$, integrate with respect to θ from 0 to π, and use the formulæ

$$\int_0^\pi \cos(m\theta)\cos(n\theta)\,d\theta = \int_0^\pi \sin(m\theta)\sin(n\theta)\,d\theta = \frac{\pi}{2}\delta_{m,n}$$

we obtain the formulæ

$$J_n(x) = \frac{1}{\pi}\int_0^\pi \cos(x\sin\theta)\cos(n\theta)\,d\theta, \quad (n \text{ even}), \quad (25.10)$$

$$J_n(x) = \frac{1}{\pi}\int_0^\pi \sin(x\sin\theta)\sin(n\theta)\,d\theta, \quad (n \text{ odd}). \quad (25.11)$$

Because of the periodic properties of the trigonometric functions we know that the integral on the right of equation (25.10) is zero if n is odd, while that on the right of equation (25.11) is zero if n is even. Thus for all integral values of n, we have

$$J_n(x) = \frac{1}{\pi}\int_0^\pi \{\cos(x\sin\theta)\cos(n\theta)+\sin(x\sin\theta)\sin(n\theta)\}d\theta$$

which is identical with the expression (25.4).

H

In particular

$$J_0(x) = \frac{1}{\pi} \int_0^\pi \cos(x \sin \theta) \, d\theta. \qquad (25.12)$$

In what follows we shall assume that the **Bessel coefficients** of the first kind are defined by equation (25.6) or, which is equivalent, by equation (25.4).

§ 26. Recurrence relations for the Bessel coefficients.
If we differentiate the generating equation (25.6) with respect to x we obtain the relation

$$\frac{1}{2}\left(t - \frac{1}{t}\right) \exp\left\{\tfrac{1}{2}x\left(t - \frac{1}{t}\right)\right\} = \sum_{n=-\infty}^{\infty} J_n'(x)t^n$$

which is equivalent to

$$\frac{1}{2} \sum_{n=-\infty}^{\infty} \{J_n(x)t^{n+1} - J_n(x)t^{n-1}\} - \sum_{n=-\infty}^{\infty} J_n'(x)t^n = 0.$$

Equating to zero the coefficient of t^n we obtain the relation

$$2J_n'(x) = J_{n-1}(x) - J_{n+1}(x). \qquad (26.1)$$

On the other hand, if we differentiate (25.6) with respect to t the resulting equation is

$$\tfrac{1}{2}x\left(1 + \frac{1}{t^2}\right) \exp\left\{\tfrac{1}{2}x\left(t - \frac{1}{t}\right)\right\} = \sum_{n=-\infty}^{\infty} nJ_n(x)t^{n-1}$$

and this is equivalent to the relation

$$\tfrac{1}{2}x \sum_{n=-\infty}^{\infty} (t^n + t^{n-2})J_n(x) - \sum_{n=-\infty}^{\infty} nJ_n(x)t^{n-1} = 0.$$

Equating the coefficient of t^{n-1} to zero we obtain the recurrence relation

$$\frac{2n}{x} J_n(x) = J_{n-1}(x) + J_{n+1}(x). \qquad (26.2)$$

Adding equations (26.1) and (26.2) we find that

$$xJ_n'(x) = xJ_{n-1}(x) - nJ_n(x) \qquad (26.3)$$

and subtracting equation (26.1) from (26.2) we obtain

$$xJ_n'(x) = nJ_n(x) - xJ_{n+1}(x). \qquad (26.4)$$

Putting $n = 0$ in this last equation we have the important special case

$$J_0'(x) = -J_1(x), \qquad (26.5)$$

and putting $n = 1$ in equation (26.3) we find that

$$J_1'(x) = J_0(x) - \frac{1}{x} J_1(x). \qquad (26.6)$$

Differentiating both sides of (26.5) with respect to x and making use of the result (26.6) we have

$$J_0''(x) = -J_0(x) + \frac{1}{x} J_1(x)$$

which, as a consequence of equation (26.6), may be written

$$J_0''(x) + \frac{1}{x} J_0'(x) + J_0(x) = 0 \qquad (26.7)$$

showing that $y = J_0(x)$ is a solution of the differential equation

$$\frac{d^2y}{dx^2} + \frac{1}{x} \frac{dy}{dx} + y = 0. \qquad (26.8)$$

We can show similarly that the Bessel function $J_n(x)$ satisfies the differential equation

$$\frac{d^2y}{dx^2} + \frac{1}{x} \frac{dy}{dx} + \left(1 - \frac{n^2}{x^2}\right) y = 0 \quad (n \text{ integral}). \quad (26.9)$$

For, from equation (26.4) we find, as a result of differentiating both sides with respect to x, that

$$xJ_n''(x) + J_n'(x) = nJ_n'(x) - J_{n+1}(x) - xJ_{n+1}'(x).$$

Now, from equation (26.4),

$$nJ_n'(x) = \frac{n^2}{x^2} J_n(x) - nJ_{n+1}(x),$$

and putting $n+1$ in place of n in equation (26.3) we see that

$$xJ_{n+1}'(x) + (n+1)J_{n+1}(x) = xJ_n(x)$$

so that

$$xJ_n''(x) + J_n'(x) = \frac{n^2}{x} J_n(x) - xJ_n(x)$$

which shows that $J_n(x)$ is a solution of equation (26.9) provided, of course, that n is an integer.

As we pointed out in § 1, equation (26.9) is known as **Bessel's equation.** What we have shown is that if the n which occurs in Bessel's equation is an integer, one solution of the equation is $J_n(x)$. It is because of this fact that Bessel coefficients are of such importance in mathematical physics, for as we saw in § 1, the equation (26.9) arises naturally in boundary value problems in mathematical physics.

§ 27. **Series expansion for the Bessel coefficients.** We shall now find the power series expansion for the Bessel coefficient $J_n(x)$. If we write

$$\exp\left\{\tfrac{1}{2}x\left(t - \frac{1}{t}\right)\right\} = \exp\left(\tfrac{1}{2}xt\right)\exp\left(-\frac{x}{2t}\right)$$

and make use of the power series for the exponential function we obtain the expansion

$$\exp\left\{\tfrac{1}{2}x\left(t - \frac{1}{t}\right)\right\} = \sum_{r=0}^{\infty} \frac{(xt)^r}{2^r r!} \sum_{s=0}^{\infty} \frac{(-x)^s}{2^s t^s s!}$$

$$= \sum_{r=0}^{\infty} \sum_{s=0}^{\infty} (-1)^s \left(\frac{x}{2}\right)^{r+s} \frac{t^{r-s}}{r! s!}. \qquad (27.1)$$

By our definition (25.6), the Bessel coefficient $J_n(x)$ is the coefficient of t^n in this expansion. If n is zero or a positive integer, we find that

$$J_n(x) = \sum_{s=0}^{\infty} \frac{(-1)^s}{s!(n+s)!} \left(\frac{x}{2}\right)^{n+2s} \qquad (27.2)$$

and when n is a negative integer we can deduce the series for $J_n(x)$ from equation (25.7).

Writing equation (27.2) in the form

$$J_n(x) = \frac{x^n}{2^n n!} \sum_{s=0}^{\infty} \frac{1}{s!(n+1)_s} (-\tfrac{1}{4}x^2)^s$$

we see that

$$J_n(x) = \frac{x^n}{2^n n!} \, {}_0F_1(n+1; -\tfrac{1}{4}x^2). \qquad (27.3)$$

The variation of the Bessel coefficients $J_0(x)$, $J_1(x)$, $J_2(x)$ for $0 \leq x \leq 20$ is shown graphically in fig. 9. These are the Bessel coefficients which occur most frequently in physical problems and their behaviour is similar to that of the general coefficient $J_n(x)$.

Simple relations for the Bessel coefficients may be derived easily from the series expansion (27.2). For example, since this equation is equivalent to

$$x^n J_n(x) = \sum_{s=0}^{\infty} \frac{(-1)^s x^{2n+2s}}{s!(n+s)!} \left(\frac{1}{2}\right)^{n+2s} \qquad (27.4)$$

it follows, as a result of differentiating both sides of this equation with respect to x, and making use of the fact that $(2n+2s)/(n+s)! = 2/(n-1+s)!$, that

$$\frac{d}{dx} \{x^n J_n(x)\} = \sum_{s=0}^{\infty} \frac{(-1)^s x^{2n+2s-1}}{s!(n-1+s)!} \left(\frac{1}{2}\right)^{n-1+2s}$$

which, by comparison with (27.4), shows that

$$\frac{d}{dx} \{x^n J_n(x)\} = x^n J_{n-1}(x). \qquad (27.5)$$

If we write this result in the form

$$\frac{1}{x}\frac{d}{dx}\{x^n J_n(x)\} = x^{n-1}J_{n-1}(x)$$

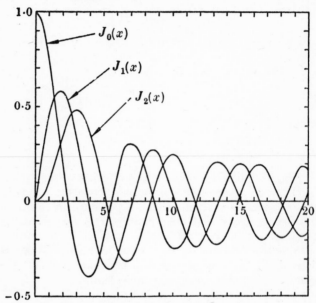

Fig. 9.   Variation of $J_0(x)$, $J_1(x)$ and $J_2(x)$ with x.

we see that if m is a positive integer less than n, then

$$\left(\frac{1}{x}\frac{d}{dx}\right)^m x^n J_n(x) = x^{n-m}J_{n-m}(x). \qquad (27.6)$$

Similarly we can establish that

$$\frac{d}{dx}\{x^{-n}J_n(x)\} = -x^{-n}J_{n+1}(x) \qquad (27.7)$$

or, which is the same thing,

$$\left(\frac{1}{x}\frac{d}{dx}\right)\{x^{-n}J_n(x)\} = -x^{-n-1}J_{n+1}(x),$$

a result which may be generalised to the form

$$\left(\frac{1}{x}\frac{d}{dx}\right)^m \{x^{-n}J_n(x)\} = (-1)^m x^{-n-m}J_{n+m}(x).$$

In particular we have the relation

$$x^{-n}J_n(x) = (-1)^n \left(\frac{1}{x}\frac{d}{dx}\right)^n J_0(x), \qquad (27.8)$$

which shows how the Bessel coefficients $J_n(x)$ may be derived from $J_0(x)$.

Another interesting property of the Bessel coefficients also follows from the power series expansion (27.3). This concerns their behaviour for small values of the argument x. Since

$$\lim_{x\to 0} {}_0F_1(n+1, -\tfrac{1}{4}x^2) = 1$$

it follows from equation (27.3) that

$$\lim_{x\to 0} x^{-n}J_n(x) = \frac{1}{2^n n!}. \qquad (27.9)$$

In other words, for small values of x, the Bessel coefficient $J_n(x)$ behaves like $x^n/2^n n!$.

§ 28. Integral expressions for the Bessel coefficients.

We have already derived one integral expression for the Bessel coefficient of order n (equation (25.4) above). In this section we shall consider other simple integral expressions for these coefficients.

We shall consider the integral

$$I = \int_{-1}^{1} (1-t^2)^{n-\frac{1}{2}} e^{ixt} dt$$

in which $n > -\frac{1}{2}$. If we develop $\exp(ixt)$ in ascending powers of ixt we see that the value of this integral is

$$\sum_{s=0}^{\infty} \frac{(ix)^s}{s!} \int_{-1}^{1} (1-t^2)^{n-\frac{1}{2}} t^s dt.$$

If s is an odd integer then the corresponding integral occurring in this series is zero, and if s is an even integer, $2r$ say, then the integral has the value

$$\int_{0}^{1} (1-u)^{n-\frac{1}{2}} u^{r-\frac{1}{2}} du = \frac{\Gamma(n+\frac{1}{2})\Gamma(r+\frac{1}{2})}{\Gamma(n+r+1)}$$

so that

$$I = \sum_{r=0}^{\infty} \frac{(-1)^r x^{2r}}{(2r)!} \frac{\Gamma(n+\frac{1}{2})\Gamma(r+\frac{1}{2})}{\Gamma(n+r+1)}$$

$$= \Gamma(\tfrac{1}{2})\Gamma(n+\tfrac{1}{2}) \sum_{r=0}^{\infty} \frac{(-1)^r x^{2r}}{r!\Gamma(n+r+1)2^{2r}}$$

since, by the duplication formula for the gamma function, $\Gamma(\tfrac{1}{2})(2r)! = 2^{2r} r! \Gamma(r+\tfrac{1}{2})$. It follows immediately from the series expansion (27.2) for $J_n(x)$ that

$$J_n(x) = \frac{(\tfrac{1}{2}x)^n}{\Gamma(\tfrac{1}{2})\Gamma(n+\tfrac{1}{2})} \int_{-1}^{1} (1-t^2)^{n-\frac{1}{2}} e^{ixt} dt \qquad (28.1)$$

and it is easily shown that this is equivalent to the formula

$$J_n(x) = \frac{x^n}{2^{n-1}\Gamma(\tfrac{1}{2})\Gamma(n+\tfrac{1}{2})} \int_{0}^{1} (1-t^2)^{n-\frac{1}{2}} \cos(xt) dt. \qquad (28.2)$$

In particular

$$J_0(x) = \frac{2}{\pi} \int_{0}^{1} \frac{\cos(xt)}{\sqrt{(1-t^2)}} dt. \qquad (28.3)$$

The result (28.2) may be expressed in a slightly different form by means of a simple change of variable. It we put

$t = \cos\theta$ we obtain the integral expression

$$J_n(x) = \frac{x^n}{2^{n-1}\Gamma(\tfrac{1}{2})\Gamma(n+\tfrac{1}{2})} \int_0^{\frac{1}{2}\pi} \cos(x\cos\theta)\sin^{2n}\theta \, d\theta, \quad (28.4)$$

while if we make the substitution $t = \sin\theta$ we get the formula

$$J_n(x) = \frac{x^n}{2^{n-1}\Gamma(\tfrac{1}{2})\Gamma(n+\tfrac{1}{2})} \int_0^{\frac{1}{2}\pi} \cos(x\sin\theta)\cos^{2n}\theta \, d\theta. \quad (28.5)$$

The particular forms appropriate to $n = 0$ are

$$J_0(x) = \frac{2}{\pi} \int_0^{\frac{1}{2}\pi} \cos(x\cos\theta) \, d\theta = \frac{2}{\pi} \int_0^{\frac{1}{2}\pi} \cos(x\sin\theta) \, d\theta. \quad (28.6)$$

§ 29. The addition formula for the Bessel coefficients.
In certain physical problems we have to reduce a Bessel coefficient of type $J_n(x+y)$ to a form more amenable to computation. We shall now derive an addition formula which is of great use in these circumstances. From the definition (25.6) we have the expansion

$$\exp\left\{\tfrac{1}{2}(x+y)\left(t-\frac{1}{t}\right)\right\} = \sum_{n=-\infty}^{\infty} J_n(x+y)t^n.$$

Writing the left-hand side as a product

$$\exp\left\{\tfrac{1}{2}x\left(t-\frac{1}{t}\right)\right\} . \exp\left\{\tfrac{1}{2}y\left(t-\frac{1}{t}\right)\right\}$$

and inserting the appropriate series from (25.6) we find that

$$\sum_{n=-\infty}^{\infty} J_n(x+y)t^n = \sum_{r=-\infty}^{\infty}\sum_{s=-\infty}^{\infty} J_r(x)J_s(y)t^{r+s}.$$

Equating coefficients of t^n we obtain the addition formula

$$J_n(x+y) = \sum_{r=-\infty}^{\infty} J_r(x)J_{n-r}(y). \quad (29.1)$$

To put this in a form which involves only Bessel coefficients of positive order we write the right-hand side in the form

$$\sum_{r=-\infty}^{-1} J_r(x)J_{n-r}(y) + \sum_{r=0}^{n} J_r(x)J_{n-r}(y) + \sum_{r=n+1}^{\infty} J_r(x)J_{n-r}(y)$$

and note that because of the relation (25.7) the first term can be written as

$$\sum_{r=-\infty}^{-1} (-1)^r J_{-r}(x)J_{n-r}(y) \equiv \sum_{r=1}^{\infty} (-1)^r J_r(x)J_{n+r}(y).$$

Similarly the third term is equal to

$$\sum_{r=1}^{\infty} J_{n+r}(x)J_{-r}(y) = \sum_{r=1}^{\infty} (-1)^r J_{n+r}(x)J_r(y)$$

so that finally we have

$$J_n(x+y) = \sum_{r=0}^{n} J_r(x)J_{n-r}(y)$$
$$+ \sum_{r=1}^{\infty} (-1)^r\{J_r(x)J_{n+r}(y) + J_{n+r}(x)J_r(y)\}. \qquad (29.2)$$

§ 30. Bessel's differential equation.

We showed previously (§ 26 above) that, if n is an integer, $J_n(x)$ is a solution of Bessel's equation (26.9). We shall now examine the solutions of that equation when the parameter n is not necessarily an integer. To emphasise that this parameter is, in general, non-integral, we shall replace it by the symbol v, so that we now consider the solutions of the second order linear differential equation

$$\frac{d^2y}{dx^2} + \frac{1}{x}\frac{dy}{dx} + \left(1 - \frac{v^2}{x^2}\right)y = 0. \qquad (30.1)$$

Writing the equation in the form

$$x^2\frac{d^2y}{dx^2} + x\frac{dy}{dx} + (-v^2 + x^2)y = 0, \qquad (30.2)$$

we see that the point $x = 0$ is a regular singular point and that in the notation of § 3, $p_0 = 1$ and $q_0 = -v^2$. The indicial equation (cf. (3.5) above) is therefore

$$\varrho^2 - v^2 = 0$$

and this has roots $\varrho = \pm v$.

First of all we shall suppose that v is neither zero nor an integer. Then the first solution is of the form

$$y = \sum_{r=0}^{\infty} c_r x^{r+v}. \tag{30.3}$$

Substituting this series in equation (30.2) we see that the coefficients c_r must be such that

$$\sum_{r=0}^{\infty} \{(v+r)(v+r-1)+(v+r)-v^2\}c_r x^{r+v} + \sum_{r=0}^{\infty} c_r x^{r+v+2} = 0.$$

Hence we must have

$$c_1\{(v+1)^2 - v^2\} = 0$$

and in general

$$c_r\{(r+v)^2 - v^2\} = -c_{r-2}, \quad (r = 2, 3, \ldots). \tag{30.4}$$

We must therefore take c_1 to be zero and hence, in order that (30.4) may be satisfied for all $r \geqq 2$, we must take

$$c_{2r+1} = 0$$

and

$$c_{2r} = \frac{(-1)^r c_0}{(2r+2v)(2r+2v-2)\ldots(2v+2)2r(2r-2)\ldots2},$$

an expression which may be put in the form

$$c_{2r} = \frac{c_0}{r!(v+1)_r}\left(-\frac{1}{4}\right)^r.$$

Taking $c_0 = 1/2^v v!$ we see that the basic solution of type

(30.3) may be taken as

$$y = \frac{x^v}{2^v \Gamma(v+1)} \sum_{r=0}^{\infty} \frac{(-\frac{1}{4}x^2)^r}{r!(v+1)_r}. \tag{30.5}$$

Comparing this series with the series (27.2) we see that it is of precisely the same form as that equation, the only difference being that n is replaced here by v. If we take the series (27.2) to define the **Bessel function of the first kind of order** n, even when n is not an integer, then we may write the solution (30.5) in the form

$$y = J_v(x).$$

Similarly, if we substitute a series of type

$$y = \sum_{r=0}^{\infty} c_r x^{r-v}$$

to correspond to the second root of the indicial equation, we find that it must be of the type

$$y = \frac{x^{-v}}{2^v \Gamma(-v+1)} \sum_{r=0}^{\infty} \frac{(-\frac{1}{4}x^2)^r}{r!(-v+1)_r} \tag{30.6}$$

and with the extension of the definition (27.2) to non-integral values of v we may write this solution in the form

$$y = J_{-v}(x).$$

Thus when v is *not* an integer we may write the general solution of equation (30.1) in the form

$$y = AJ_v(x) + BJ_{-v}(x) \tag{30.7}$$

where $J_v(x)$ is defined by the equation

$$J_v(x) = \frac{x^v}{2^v \Gamma(v+1)} {}_0F_1(v+1; -\frac{1}{4}x^2). \tag{30.8}$$

It should be observed that the results of §§ 27, 28, with the exception of (27.8), are true when n is not an integer, since they were derived directly from the definition (27.2), which is equivalent to (30.8). The transition is effected merely by replacing $n!$ by $\Gamma(v+1)$.

When v is zero or an integer we know from equation (25.7) that the solutions $J_v(x)$ and $J_{-v}(x)$ are not linearly independent. We must therefore use the formulæ (3.8) to calculate the second solution.

We shall consider first the case in which $v = 0$. If we let

$$w = \sum_{r=0}^{\infty} c_r x^{r+\varrho}$$

then in order to satisfy the recurrence relation (30.4) we must have

$$w = x^\varrho \sum_{r=0}^{\infty} \frac{(-\tfrac{1}{4}x)^r}{r!(\varrho+1)_r} \tag{30.9}$$

and putting $\varrho = 0$ we obtain the first solution

$$w_0 = J_0(x). \tag{30.10}$$

Using the result

$$\frac{\partial}{\partial \varrho} \frac{1}{(\varrho+1)_r} = -\frac{1}{(\varrho+1)_r} \left\{ \sum_{s=1}^{r} \frac{1}{\varrho+s} \right\}$$

we see that

$$\frac{\partial w}{\partial \varrho} = w \log x - x^\varrho \sum_{r=1}^{\infty} \frac{(-\tfrac{1}{4}x)^r}{r!(\varrho+1)_r} \left\{ \sum_{s=1}^{r} \frac{1}{\varrho+s} \right\}.$$

Putting $\varrho = 0$ and substituting the value (30.10) for w_0 we find that the second solution $(\partial w/\partial \varrho)_{\varrho=0}$ is

$$\mathsf{Y}_0(x) = J_0(x) \log x - \sum_{r=1}^{\infty} \frac{(-\tfrac{1}{4}x)^r}{(r!)^2} \phi(r), \tag{30.11}$$

where

$$\phi(r) = \sum_{s=1}^{r} \frac{1}{s}. \tag{30.12}$$

The function $\mathsf{Y}_0(x)$ so obtained is called **Neumann's Bessel function of the second kind of zero order.** Obviously if we add to $Y_0(x)$ a function which is a constant multiple of $J_0(x)$ the resulting function is also a solution of the differential equation

$$\frac{d^2y}{dx^2} + \frac{1}{x}\frac{dy}{dx} + y = 0. \tag{30.13}$$

In particular the function

$$Y_0(x) = \frac{2}{\pi}\{Y_0(x) - (\log 2 - \gamma)J_0(x)\},$$

where γ denotes Euler's constant, will be a second solution of the equation. Substituting from equation (30.11) for $Y_0(x)$ in this equation we obtain the expression

$$Y_0(x) = \frac{2}{\pi}\{\log(\tfrac{1}{2}x) + \gamma\}J_0(x) - \frac{2}{\pi}\sum_{r=1}^{\infty}\frac{(-\tfrac{1}{4}x^2)^r}{(r!)^2}\phi(r) \tag{30.14}$$

where $\phi(r)$ is defined by equation (30.12).

The function $Y_0(x)$ so defined is known as **Weber's Bessel function of the second kind of zero order**.

Thus the complete solution of the equation (30.13) is

$$y = AJ_0(x) + BY_0(x) \tag{30.15}$$

where A, B are arbitrary constants and $J_0(x)$, $Y_0(x)$ are given by equations (30.8) and (30.14) respectively.

It can be shown by an exactly similar process that when v is an integer the complete solution of the equation (30.1) is

$$y = AJ_v(x) + BY_v(x) \tag{30.16}$$

where A, B are arbitrary constants, $J_v(x)$ is defined by equation (30.8) and $Y_v(x)$ is given by

$$Y_v(x) = \frac{2}{\pi}\{\gamma + \log(\tfrac{1}{2}x)\}J_v(x) - \frac{1}{\pi}\sum_{r=0}^{v-1}\frac{(v-r-1)!}{r!}\left(\frac{2}{x}\right)^{v-2r}$$

$$-\frac{1}{\pi}\sum_{r=0}^{\infty}\frac{(-1)^r(\tfrac{1}{2}x)^{v+2r}}{r!(v+r)!}\{\phi(r+v) + \phi(r)\}. \tag{30.17}$$

The function $Y_v(x)$ so defined † reduces to the $Y_0(x)$ of equation (30.14) as $v \to 0$ and is known as **Weber's Bessel function of the second kind of order v.**

The variation of $Y_0(x)$ and $Y_1(x)$ for a range of values of x is shown graphically in fig. 10.

The functions $J_v(x)$ and $Y_v(x)$ are independent solutions of the equation (30.1), but in certain circumstances it is

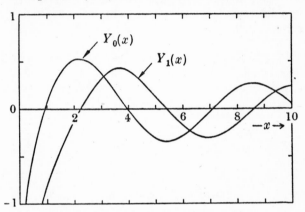

Fig. 10.   Variation of $Y_0(x)$ and $Y_1(x)$ with x.

advantageous to define, in terms of them, two new independent solutions. If we write

$$H_v^{(1)}(x) = J_v(x) + iY_v(x), \qquad (30.18)$$

$$H_v^{(2)}(x) = J_v(x) - iY_v(x), \qquad (30.19)$$

then it is obvious that we can take the general solution of Bessel's differential equation (30.1) to be

$$y = A_1 H_v^{(1)}(x) + A_2 H_v^{(2)}(x), \qquad (30.20)$$

where A_1 and A_2 are arbitrary constants. The functions $H_v^{(1)}(x)$, $H_v^{(2)}(x)$ defined by equations (30.18) and (30.19)

† This function is denoted as $N_v(x)$ by Courant and Hilbert.

are called **Hankel's Bessel functions of the third kind of order** v.

The Hankel functions $H_v^{(1)}(x)$ and $H_v^{(2)}(x)$ bear the same relation to the Bessel functions $J_v(x)$, $Y_v(x)$ as the functions $\exp(\pm ivx)$ bear to $\cos vx$ and $\sin vx$, and are used in analysis for similar reasons. It should also be noted that the Bessel functions $Y_v(x)$, $H_v^{(1)}(x)$, $H_v^{(2)}(x)$ satisfy the same differential equations and recurrence relations as the function $J_v(x)$.

§ 31. Spherical Bessel functions.

A problem which arises in mathematical physics is that of the solution of the wave equation in spherical polar coordinates

$$\frac{\partial^2 \psi}{\partial r^2} + \frac{2}{r}\frac{\partial \psi}{\partial r} + \frac{1}{r^2 \sin\theta}\frac{\partial}{\partial\theta}\left(\sin\theta\,\frac{\partial \psi}{\partial\theta}\right)$$
$$+ \frac{1}{r^2 \sin^2\theta}\frac{\partial^2 \psi}{\partial\phi^2} = \frac{1}{c^2}\frac{\partial^2 \psi}{\partial t^2}. \qquad (31.1)$$

If we take a solution of this equation of the form

$$\psi = Y_{m,\,n}(\theta,\,\phi)\psi(r)e^{i\omega t}, \qquad (31.2)$$

where $Y_{m,\,n}(\theta,\,\phi)$ is the surface spherical harmonic defined by equation (23.3) and $\psi(r)$ is a function of r alone which satisfies the equation

$$\frac{d^2\Psi}{dr^2} + \frac{2}{r}\frac{d\Psi}{dr} - \frac{n(n+1)}{r^2}\Psi + \frac{\omega^2}{c^2}\Psi = 0. \qquad (31.3)$$

Now putting

$$\Psi = r^{-\frac{1}{2}}R \qquad (31.4)$$

we see that equation (31.3) becomes

$$\frac{d^2R}{dr^2} + \frac{1}{r}\frac{dR}{dr} + \left\{\frac{\omega^2}{c^2} - \frac{(n+\frac{1}{2})^2}{r^2}\right\}R = 0$$

whose general solution is readily seen to be

$$R = AJ_{n+\frac{1}{2}}(\omega r/c) + BJ_{-n-\frac{1}{2}}(\omega r/c). \qquad (31.5)$$

Hence the function

$$\psi = Y_{m,\,n}(\theta,\,\phi)J_{\pm(n+\frac{1}{2})}(\omega r/c)e^{i\omega t} \qquad (31.6)$$

is a solution of the equation (31.1).

The functions $J_{\pm(n+\frac{1}{2})}(x)$ which occur in the solution (31.6) are called **spherical Bessel functions.** We shall now show that they are related simply to the circular functions. First of all we consider the Bessel function $J_{\frac{1}{2}}(x)$. If we let $v = \frac{1}{2}$ in equation (30.6) and make use of the duplication formula for the gamma function we obtain the result

$$J_{\frac{1}{2}}(x) = \left(\frac{2}{\pi x}\right)^{\frac{1}{2}} \sum_{r=0}^{\infty} \frac{(-1)^r x^{2r+1}}{(2r+1)!}$$

which shows that

$$J_{\frac{1}{2}}(x) = \left(\frac{2}{\pi x}\right)^{\frac{1}{2}} \sin x. \qquad (31.7)$$

Again, if we put $v = -\frac{1}{2}$ in equation (30.6) we obtain the relation

$$J_{-\frac{1}{2}}(x) = \left(\frac{2}{\pi x}\right)^{\frac{1}{2}} \cos x. \qquad (31.8)$$

The other functions $J_m(x)$ where m is half an odd integer may be worked out in a similar fashion. It is left as an exercise to the reader to show that

$$J_m(x) = \left(\frac{2}{\pi x}\right)^{\frac{1}{2}} \{f_m(x) \sin x - g_m(x) \cos x\},$$

$$J_{-m}(x) = \left(\frac{2}{\pi x}\right)^{\frac{1}{2}} (-1)^{n-\frac{1}{2}}\{g_m(x) \sin x + f_m(x) \cos x\},$$

where the functions f_m, g_m are given in Table 1.

I

These functions which arise in the way described have been tabulated in *Tables of Spherical Bessel Functions* 2 vols. (Columbia Univ. Press, 1947) prepared by the Mathematical Tables Project of the National Bureau of Standards.

Table 1

m	f_m	g_m
$\dfrac{3}{2}$	$\dfrac{1}{x}$	1
$\dfrac{5}{2}$	$\dfrac{3}{x^2} - 1$	$\dfrac{3}{x}$
$\dfrac{7}{2}$	$\dfrac{15}{x^3} - \dfrac{6}{x}$	$\dfrac{15}{x^2} - 1$
$\dfrac{9}{2}$	$\dfrac{105}{x^4} - \dfrac{45}{x^2} + 1$	$\dfrac{105}{x^3} - \dfrac{10}{x}$
$\dfrac{11}{2}$	$\dfrac{945}{x^5} - \dfrac{420}{x^3} + \dfrac{15}{x}$	$\dfrac{945}{x^4} - \dfrac{105}{x^2} + 1$

§ 32. Integrals involving Bessel functions. In this section we shall derive the values of some integrals involving Bessel functions which arise in practical applications. In the first instance we shall consider definite integrals.

From equation (27.5) we have the relation

$$\int_0^\alpha x^n J_{n-1}(x)\,dx = \left[x^n J_n(x)\right]_0^\alpha.$$

If $n > 0$, $x^n J_n(x) \to 0$ as $x \to 0$ so that the lower limit is zero and we obtain the integral

$$\int_0^\alpha x^n J_{n-1}(x)dx = \alpha^n J_n(\alpha), \quad (n>0), \tag{32.1}$$

which, by a simple change of variable, gives the result

$$\int_0^a r^n J_{n-1}(\xi r)dr = \frac{a^n}{\xi} J_n(\xi a), \quad (n>0). \tag{32.2}$$

A particular case of this result which is of frequent use in mathematical physics is obtained by putting $n = 1$ in equation (32.2). In this way we obtain the integral

$$\int_0^a r J_0(\xi r)dr = \frac{a}{\xi} J_1(a\xi). \tag{32.3}$$

Further results may be obtained from (32.2) by familiar devices such as integration by parts. For example, making use of equation (27.5) we may write

$$\int_0^a r^3 J_0(\xi r)dr = \int_0^a r^2 \frac{1}{\xi} \frac{\partial}{\partial r} \{r J_1(\xi r)\}dr,$$

and, integrating by parts, we see that the right-hand side of this equation becomes

$$\frac{a^3}{\xi} J_1(\xi a) - \frac{2}{\xi} \int_0^a r^2 J_1(\xi r)dr$$

which reduces, by virtue of (32.2), to

$$\frac{a^3}{\xi} J_1(\xi a) - \frac{2a^2}{\xi^2} J_2(\xi a).$$

Now by the recurrence relation (26.2) we have the expression

$$J_2(\xi a) = \frac{2}{\xi a} J_1(\xi a) - J_0(\xi a)$$

so that finally we have the result

$$\int_0^a r^3 J_0(\xi r)dr = \frac{2a^2}{\xi^2}\left\{J_0(\xi a) + \left(\tfrac{1}{2}a\xi - \frac{2}{a\xi}\right)J_1(a\xi)\right\}. \quad (32.4)$$

Combining this result with equation (32.3) we obtain the integral

$$\int_0^a r(a^2 - r^2)J_0(\xi r)dr = \frac{4a}{\xi^3}J_1(\xi a) - \frac{2a^2}{\xi^2}J_0(\xi a). \quad (32.5)$$

The most commonly occurring infinite integrals are most easily evaluated by means of substituting the formula (27.3) in parts (ii) and (iii) of example 17 of Chapter II. From part (ii) of that example we see that

$$\frac{a^v}{2^v\Gamma(v+1)}\int_0^\infty {}_0F_1(v+1;\ -\tfrac{1}{4}a^2x^2)x^{v+\mu}e^{-px}dx$$

$$= \frac{\Gamma(\mu+v+1)a^v}{2^v\Gamma(v+1)p^{\mu+v+1}}$$

$$\qquad {}_2F_1\left(\tfrac{1}{2}\mu+\tfrac{1}{2}v+\tfrac{1}{2},\ \tfrac{1}{2}\mu+\tfrac{1}{2}v+1;\ v+1;\ -\frac{a^2}{p^2}\right). \quad (32.6)$$

If we make use of equation (30.8) on the left-hand side of this equation and of equation (7.4) on the right-hand side, we see that this result is equivalent to the formula

$$\int_0^\infty J_v(ax)x^\mu e^{-px}dx = \frac{\Gamma(\mu+v+1)a^v}{2^v\Gamma(v+1)(a^2+p^2)^{\frac{1}{2}\mu+\frac{1}{2}v+\frac{1}{2}}}$$

$$\qquad \times {}_2F_1\left(\tfrac{1}{2}\mu+\tfrac{1}{2}v+\tfrac{1}{2};\ \tfrac{1}{2}v-\tfrac{1}{2}\mu;\ v+1;\ \frac{a^2}{a^2+p^2}\right), \quad (32.7)$$

where $p>0$, $\mu+v>0$.

The hypergeometric series occurring on the right-hand of this equation assumes a particularly simple form if either

$\mu = v$ or $\mu = v+1$, and we obtain the formulae

$$\int_0^\infty J_v(ax)x^v e^{-px}dx = \frac{2^v \Gamma(v+\frac{1}{2})}{\Gamma(\frac{1}{2})} \cdot \frac{a^v}{(a^2+p^2)^{v+\frac{1}{2}}}, \quad (32.8)$$

$$\int_0^\infty J_v(ax)x^{v+1} e^{-px}dx = \frac{2^{v+1} \Gamma(v+\frac{3}{2})}{\Gamma(\frac{1}{2})} \cdot \frac{pa^v}{(a^2+p^2)^{v+\frac{3}{2}}}. \quad (32.9)$$

Two special cases of the formula (32.8) which occur frequently are

$$\int_0^\infty J_0(ax)e^{-px}dx = \frac{1}{\sqrt{(a^2+p^2)}}, \quad (32.10)$$

$$\int_0^\infty xJ_1(ax)e^{-px}dx = \frac{a}{(a^2+p^2)^{\frac{3}{2}}}. \quad (32.11)$$

Integrating both sides of equation (32.11) with respect to p from p to ∞ we find that

$$\int_0^\infty J_1(ax)e^{-px}dx = \frac{1}{a} - \frac{p}{a\sqrt{(a^2+p^2)}}. \quad (32.12)$$

A special case of (32.9) which is often needed is

$$\int_0^\infty xJ_0(ax)e^{-px}dx = \frac{p}{(a^2+p^2)^{\frac{3}{2}}}. \quad (32.13)$$

If we let p tend to zero on both sides of equation (32.7) we find that we can sum the hypergeometric series by Gauss's theorem (7.2) provided that $|\mu| < |v+1|$. We then have the result

$$\int_0^\infty J_v(ax)x^\mu dx = \frac{2^\mu \Gamma(\frac{1}{2}+\frac{1}{2}\mu+\frac{1}{2}v)}{a^{\mu+1}\Gamma(\frac{1}{2}-\frac{1}{2}\mu+\frac{1}{2}v)}. \quad (32.14)$$

Similarly from part (iii) of example 17 of Chapter II

we have the equation

$$\int_0^\infty {}_0F_1(v+1; -\tfrac{1}{4}a^2x^2)e^{-p^2x^2}x^{\mu+v-1}dx$$

$$= \frac{\Gamma(\tfrac{1}{2}\mu+\tfrac{1}{2}v)}{2p^{\mu+v}} {}_1F_1\left(\tfrac{1}{2}\mu+\tfrac{1}{2}v; v+1; -\frac{a^2}{4p^2}\right)$$

which, because of (27.3), is equivalent to

$$\int_0^\infty J_v(ax)e^{-p^2x^2}x^{\mu-1}dx$$

$$= \frac{a^v\Gamma(\tfrac{1}{2}\mu+\tfrac{1}{2}v)}{2^{v+1}p^{\mu+v}\Gamma(v+1)} {}_1F_1\left(\tfrac{1}{2}\mu+\tfrac{1}{2}v; v+1; -\frac{a^2}{4p^2}\right). \quad (32.15)$$

From parts (i) and (ii) of example 11 of Chapter II we have the special cases

$$\int_0^\infty x^{v+1}J_v(ax)e^{-p^2x^2}dx = \frac{a^v e^{-a^2/4p^2}}{(2p^2)^{v+1}}, \qquad (32.16)$$

and

$$\int_0^\infty x^{v+3}J_v(ax)e^{-p^2x^2}dx = \frac{a^v}{2^{v+1}p^{2v+4}}\left(v+1-\frac{a^2}{4p^2}\right)e^{-a^2/4p^2} \qquad (32.17)$$

of which the most frequently used are

$$\int_0^\infty xJ_0(ax)e^{-p^2x^2}dx = \frac{1}{2p^2}e^{-a^2/4p^2} \qquad (32.18)$$

and

$$\int_0^\infty x^3J_0(ax)e^{-p^2x^2}dx = \frac{1}{2p^4}\left(1-\frac{a^2}{4p^2}\right)e^{-a^2/4p^2}. \quad (32.19)$$

§ 33. The modified Bessel functions. By an argument similar to that employed in § 1 we can readily show that

Laplace's equation in cylindrical coordinates

$$\frac{\partial^2 \psi}{\partial \varrho^2} + \frac{1}{\varrho} \frac{\partial \psi}{\partial \varrho} + \frac{1}{\varrho^2} \frac{\partial^2 \psi}{\partial \phi^2} + \frac{\partial^2 \psi}{\partial z^2} = 0$$

possesses solutions of the form

$$\psi = e^{\pm i v \phi \pm i m z} R(\varrho)$$

where $R(\varrho)$ satisfies the ordinary differential equation

$$\frac{d^2 R}{d\varrho^2} + \frac{1}{\varrho} \frac{dR}{d\varrho} - \left(m^2 + \frac{v^2}{\varrho^2} \right) R = 0. \tag{33.1}$$

Writing x in place of $m\varrho$ we see that this equation is equivalent to the equation

$$\frac{d^2 R}{dx^2} + \frac{1}{x} \frac{dR}{dx} - \left(1 + \frac{v^2}{x^2} \right) R = 0. \tag{33.2}$$

If we proceed in exactly the same way as in § 30 we can show that if v is neither zero nor an integer the solution of this equation is

$$R = A I_v(x) + B I_{-v}(x) \tag{33.3}$$

where A and B are arbitrary constants and the function $I_v(x)$ is defined by the equation

$$I_v(x) = \frac{x^v}{2^v \Gamma(v+1)} \sum_{r=0}^{\infty} \frac{(\tfrac{1}{4} x^2)^r}{r!(v+1)_r}$$

$$= \frac{x^v}{2^v \Gamma(v+1)} \, {}_0 F_1(v+1; \tfrac{1}{4} x^2). \tag{33.4}$$

Comparing equation (33.4) with equation (30.8) we see that

$$I_v(x) = i^{-v} J_v(ix) \tag{33.5}$$

a result which might have been conjectured from the differential equation itself.

If v is an integer, n say, then $I_{-n}(x)$ is a multiple of $I_n(x)$ so that the solution (33.3) in effect contains only one arbitrary constant. By a process similar to that outlined in § 30 we can show that in these circumstances the general solution of equation (34.2) is

$$R = AI_n(x) + BK_n(x) \tag{33.6}$$

where the function $K_n(x)$ is defined by the equation

$$K_n(x) = (-1)^{n+1}I_n(x)\{\log\left(\tfrac{1}{2}x\right) + \gamma\}$$

$$+ \tfrac{1}{2}\sum_{r=0}^{n-1} \frac{(-1)^r(n-r-1)!}{r!}\left(\tfrac{1}{2}x\right)^{-n+2r}$$

$$+ \tfrac{1}{2}(-1)^n\sum_{r=1}^{\infty} \frac{1}{r!(n+r)!}\{\phi(r)+\phi(n+r)\}\left(\tfrac{1}{2}x\right)^{n+2r}. \tag{33.7}$$

The functions $I_n(x)$, $K_n(x)$ defined by equations (34.4) and (34.7) respectively are known as **modified Bessel functions** of the first and second kinds.

The result (33.5) is very useful for deducing properties of the modified Bessel function $I_n(x)$ from those of the Bessel function $J_n(x)$. For instance, when n is an integer it follows from equation (25.7) that

$$I_{-n}(x) = I_n(x) \tag{33.8}$$

and from equations (26.1) to (26.5) respectively that

$$2I'_n(x) = I_{n-1}(x) + I_{n+1}(x), \tag{33.9}$$

$$\frac{2n}{x}I_n(x) = I_{n-1}(x) - I_{n+1}(x), \tag{33.10}$$

$$xI'_n(x) = xI_{n-1}(x) - nI_n(x), \tag{33.11}$$

$$xI'_n(x) = nI_n(x) + xI_{n+1}(x), \tag{33.12}$$

$$I'_0(x) = I_1(x). \tag{33.13}$$

Similarly equations (27.5) and (27.7) imply the relations

$$\frac{d}{dx}\{x^n I_n(x)\} = x^n I_{n-1}(x) \tag{33.14}$$

$$\frac{d}{dx}\{x^{-n} I_n(x)\} = x^{-n} I_{n+1}(x). \tag{33.15}$$

All of these relations can, of course, be derived directly from the definition (33.4) of $I_\nu(x)$ and it is suggested as an exercise to the reader to derive them in this way.

It should also be observed that $K_n(x)$ satisfies the same recurrence relations as $I_n(x)$.

The variation of $I_0(x)$, $I_1(x)$ and $I_2(x)$ with x is shown graphically in fig. 11 and that of $K_0(x)$, $K_1(x)$ and $K_2(x)$ is shown in fig. 12.

§ 34. The Ber and Bei functions.

If we wish to find solutions of the form

$$\psi = R(\varrho)e^{i\omega t}$$

of the diffusion equation

$$\frac{\partial^2 \psi}{\partial \varrho^2} + \frac{1}{\varrho}\frac{\partial \psi}{\partial \varrho} = \frac{1}{\kappa}\frac{\partial \psi}{\partial t}$$

we have to solve the ordinary differential equation

$$\frac{d^2 R}{d\varrho^2} + \frac{1}{\varrho}\frac{dR}{d\varrho} - \frac{i\omega}{\kappa}R = 0.$$

On changing the independent variable to $x = (\omega/\kappa)^{\frac{1}{2}}\varrho$ we see that this latter equation is equivalent to the equation

$$\frac{d^2 R}{dx^2} + \frac{1}{x}\frac{dR}{dx} - iR = 0. \tag{34.1}$$

Formally we may take the independent solutions of

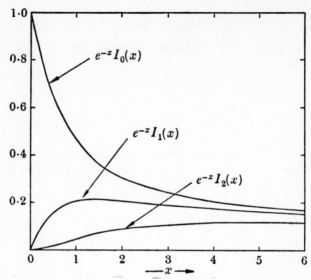

Fig. 11.—Variation of $e^{-x}I_0(x)$, $e^{-x}I_1(x)$ and $e^{-x}I_2(x)$ with x.

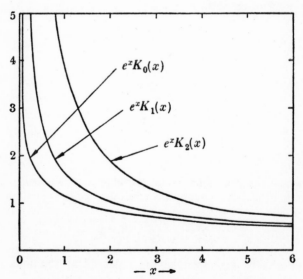

Fig. 12. Variation of $e^x K_0(x)$, $e^x K_1(x)$ and $e^x K_2(x)$ with x.

this equation to be $I_0(i^{\frac{1}{2}}x)$ and $K_0(i^{\frac{1}{2}}x)$. Kelvin introduced two new functions ber(x) and bei(x) which are respectively the real and imaginary parts of $I_0(i^{\frac{1}{2}}x)$, i.e.

$$\text{ber}\,(x) + i\,\text{bei}\,(x) = I_0(i^{\frac{1}{2}}x). \tag{34.2}$$

From the definition (33.4) of $I_0(x)$ we see that

$$\text{ber}\,(x) = \sum_{s=0}^{\infty} \frac{(-1)^s(\tfrac{1}{4}x^2)^{2s}}{(2s!)^2}, \tag{34.3}$$

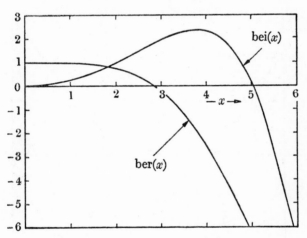

Fig. 13.   Variation of ber(x) and bei(x) with x.

and that

$$\text{bei}\,(x) = \sum_{s=0}^{\infty} \frac{(-1)^s(\tfrac{1}{4}x^2)^{2s+1}}{(2s+1)!^2}. \tag{34.4}$$

The variation of the functions ber(x) and bei(x) with x is shown diagrammatically in fig. 13.

In a similar way the functions ker(x) and kei(x) are defined to be respectively the real and imaginary parts of the complex function $K_0(i^{\frac{1}{2}}x)$, i.e.

$$\ker(x) + i\,\text{kei}(x) = K_0(i^{\frac{1}{2}}x). \tag{34.5}$$

From the definition (33.7) of $K_0(x)$ we can readily show that

$$\ker(x) = -\{\log(\tfrac{1}{2}x) + \gamma\}\,\text{ber}(x) + \tfrac{1}{4}\pi\,\text{bei}(x)$$
$$+ \sum_{r=1}^{\infty} \frac{(-1)^r(\tfrac{1}{2}x)^{4r}}{(2r)!^2}\,\phi(2r), \tag{34.6}$$

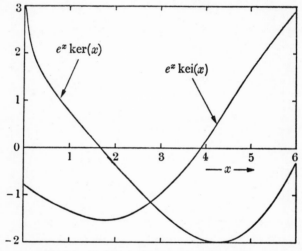

Fig. 14.   Variation of ker(x) and kei(x) with x.

and that

$$\text{kei}(x) = -\{\log(\tfrac{1}{2}x) + \gamma\}\,\text{bei}(x) - \tfrac{1}{4}\pi\,\text{ber}(x)$$
$$+ \sum_{r=0}^{\infty} \frac{(-1)^r(\tfrac{1}{2}x)^{4r+2}}{(2r+1)!^2}\,\phi(2r+1). \tag{34.7}$$

Fig. 14 shows the variation of the functions $\ker(x)$ and $\text{kei}(x)$ over a range of values of the independent variable x.

The four functions ber, bei, ker and kei are used more often in electrical engineering than they are in physics or chemistry. For a full account of their properties and those of their generalisation to higher order and of their application to engineering problems the reader is referred to N. W. McLachlan's *Bessel Functions for Engineers* (Oxford University Press, 1934).

§ 35. Expansions in series of Bessel functions.

We know from § 30 that

$$\left\{ x^2 \frac{d^2}{dx^2} + x \frac{d}{dx} + (\lambda^2 x^2 - m^2) \right\} J_m(\lambda x) = 0, \qquad (35.1)$$

$$\left\{ x^2 \frac{d^2}{dx^2} + x \frac{d}{dx} + (\mu^2 x^2 - n^2) \right\} J_n(\mu x) = 0, \qquad (35.2)$$

so that multiplying equation (35.1) by $J_n(\mu x)/x$, (35.2) by $J_m(\lambda x)/x$, integrating with respect to x from 0 to a and subtracting we find that

$$(\lambda^2 - \mu^2) \int_0^a x J_m(\lambda x) J_n(\mu x) dx + (n^2 - m^2) \int_0^a J_m(\lambda x) J_n(\mu x) \frac{dx}{x}$$

$$= a[\mu J_n(\lambda a) J_m'(\mu a) - \lambda J_n(\mu a) J_m'(\lambda a)], \quad (35.3)$$

if $n > -1$, $m > -1$.

Putting $m = n$ in this result we find that if $\lambda \neq \mu$,

$$\int_0^a x J_n(\lambda x) J_n(\mu x) dx$$

$$= \frac{a}{\lambda^2 - \mu^2} \left[\mu J_n(\lambda a) J_n'(\mu a) - \lambda J_n(\mu a) J_n'(\lambda a) \right]. \quad (35.4)$$

The corresponding expression for $\lambda = \mu$ is obtained by putting $\mu = \lambda + \varepsilon$, where ε is small, using Taylor's theorem and then letting ε tend to zero. We find that

$$\int_0^a x\{J_n(\lambda x)\}^2 dx$$
$$= \tfrac{1}{2}a^2\left[\{J_n'(\lambda a)\}^2 + \left(1 - \frac{n^2}{\lambda^2 a^2}\right)\right]\{J_n(\lambda a)\}^2. \quad (35.5)$$

Suppose now that λ and μ are positive roots of the transcendental equation

$$hJ_n(\lambda a) + k\lambda aJ_n'(\lambda a) = 0 \quad (35.6)$$

where h and k are constants. It follows then that

$$\int_0^a xJ_n(\lambda x)J_n(\mu x)dx = c_\lambda \delta_{\lambda,\,\mu} \quad (35.7)$$

where

$$c_\lambda = \frac{\{J_n(\lambda a)\}^2}{2k^2\lambda^2}\{k^2\lambda^2 a^2 + h^2 - k^2 n^2\}. \quad (35.8)$$

If we now suppose that we can expand an arbitrary function $f(x)$ in the form

$$f(x) = \sum_i a_i J_n(\lambda_i x) \quad (35.9)$$

where the sum is taken over the positive roots of the equation (35.6) then we can determine the coefficients a_i as follows: Multiply both sides of equation (35.9) by $xJ_n(\lambda_j x)$ and integrate with respect to x from 0 to a; then

$$\int_0^a xf(x)J_n(\lambda_j x)dx = \sum_i a_i \int_0^a xJ_n(\lambda_i x)J_n(\lambda_j x)dx$$

from which it follows that

$$a_j = \frac{1}{c_\lambda}\int_0^a xf(x)J_n(\lambda_j x)dx. \quad (35.10)$$

Because of its similarity to a Fourier series, a series of the type (35.9) is called a Fourier-Bessel series.

In particular if the sum is taken over the roots of the equation

$$J_n'(\lambda a) = 0 \tag{35.11}$$

then the coefficients of the sum (35.9) are given by

$$a_j = \frac{2\lambda_j^2}{\{J_n(\lambda_j a)\}^2} \cdot \frac{1}{(\lambda_j^2 a^2 - n^2)} \int_0^a x f(x) J_n(\lambda_j x) dx. \tag{35.12}$$

Similarly if the sum is taken over the positive roots of the equation

$$J_n(\lambda a) = 0 \tag{35.13}$$

we find that the coefficients a_j are given by the formula

$$a_j = \frac{2}{a^2 \{J_n'(\lambda_j a)\}^2} \int_0^a x f(x) J_n(\lambda_j x) dx. \tag{35.14}$$

In this section no attempt has been made to discuss the very difficult problem of the convergence of Fourier-Bessel series. For a very full discussion of this topic the reader is referred to Chapter XVIII of G. N. Watson's *A Treatise on the Theory of Bessel Functions*, 2nd edition (Cambridge University Press, 1944).

§ 36. The use of Bessel functions in potential theory.

As an example of the use of Bessel functions in potential theory we shall consider the problem of determining a function $\psi(\varrho, z)$ for the half-space $a \geqq \varrho \geqq 0$, $z \geqq 0$ satisfying the differential equation

$$\frac{\partial^2 \psi}{\partial \varrho^2} + \frac{1}{\varrho} \frac{\partial \psi}{\partial \varrho} + \frac{\partial^2 \psi}{\partial z^2} = 0 \tag{36.1}$$

and the boundary conditions:

(i) $\psi = f(\varrho)$, on $z = 0$;

(ii) $\psi \to 0$ as $z \to \infty$;

(iii) $\dfrac{\partial \psi}{\partial \varrho} + \kappa \psi = 0$ on $\varrho = a$;

(iv) ψ remains finite as $\varrho \to 0$.

We saw in § 1 that a function of the form $\psi = R(\varrho)Z(z)$ is a solution of equation (36.1) provided that

$$\frac{d^2 Z}{dz^2} - \lambda_i^2 Z = 0 \qquad (36.2)$$

and that

$$\frac{d^2 R}{d\varrho^2} + \frac{1}{\varrho} \frac{dR}{d\varrho} + \lambda_i^2 R = 0 \qquad (36.3)$$

where λ_i is a constant of separation. To satisfy the boundary condition (ii) we must take solutions of equation (36.2) of the form

$$Z = e^{-\lambda_i z}$$

and to satisfy the condition (iv) we must take as the solutions of equation (36.3) functions of the form

$$R = J_0(\lambda_i \varrho)$$

since the second solutions $Y_0(\lambda_i \varrho)$ would become infinite in the region of the axis $\varrho = 0$.

The differential equation (36.1) and the boundary conditions (ii) and (iv) are satisfied by any sums of the form

$$\psi(\rho,\, z) = \sum_i a_i e^{-\lambda_i z} J_0(\lambda_i \varrho) \qquad (36.4)$$

where the a_i and λ_i are constants. But if we are to satisfy the boundary condition (iii) we must take the sum over the positive roots of the equation †

$$\lambda_i J_0'(\lambda_i a) + \kappa J_0(\lambda_i a) = 0. \qquad (36.5)$$

† For properties of the roots of this equation see example 16, p. 144.

The solution is determined therefore if we can find constants a_i such that condition (i) is satisfied, i.e. such that

$$f(\varrho) = \sum_i a_i J_0(\lambda_i \varrho). \tag{36.6}$$

From equations (35.10) and (35.8) we see that we must take

$$a_i = \frac{2\lambda_i^2}{a^2(\lambda_i^2 + \kappa^2)\{J_0(\lambda_i a)\}^2} \int_0^a \varrho' f(\varrho') J_0(\lambda_i \varrho') d\varrho'. \tag{36.7}$$

Hence the required solution is

$$\psi(\rho, z) = \frac{2}{a^2} \sum_i \frac{\lambda_i^2 e^{-\lambda_i z} J_0(\lambda_i \varrho)}{(\lambda_i^2 + \kappa^2)\{J_0(\lambda_i a)\}^2} \int_0^a \varrho' f(\varrho') J_0(\lambda_i \varrho') d\varrho' \tag{36.8}$$

where the sum is taken over the positive roots of the equation (36.5).

If, instead of the boundary condition (iii), we had the condition $\psi = 0$ on $\varrho = a$ then it is easily seen that the solution would have been

$$\psi(\rho, z) = \frac{2}{a^2} \sum_i \frac{e^{-\lambda_i z} J_0(\lambda_i \varrho)}{\{J_1(\lambda_i a)\}^2} \int_0^a \varrho' f(\varrho') J_0(\lambda_i \varrho') d\varrho' \tag{36.9}$$

where the sum is taken over the positive roots λ_i of the transcendental equation

$$J_0(\lambda a) = 0. \tag{36.10}$$

For example suppose that ψ satisfies the conditions $\psi = 0$ on $\varrho = a$, $\psi \to 0$ as $z \to \infty$, $\psi = \psi_0(a^2 - \varrho^2)$ on $z = 0$, $0 \leq \varrho \leq a$, then the solution to the problem is given by equation (36.9) with $f(\varrho') = \psi_0(a^2 - \varrho'^2)$. By equation (32.5) we have

$$\int_0^a \varrho' f(\varrho') J_0(\lambda_i \varrho') d\varrho' = \frac{4a\psi_0}{\lambda_i^3} J_1(\lambda_i a) - \frac{2a^2\psi}{\lambda_i^2} J_0(\lambda_i a)$$

$$= \frac{4a\psi_0}{\lambda_i^3} J_1(\lambda_i a)$$

K

since λ_i is a root of equation (36.10). Thus the required solution is

$$\dot{\psi}(\rho, z) = \frac{8\psi_0}{a} \sum_i \frac{e^{-\lambda_i z} J_0(\lambda_i \varrho)}{\lambda_i^3 J_1(\lambda_i a)}. \qquad (36.11)$$

Tables of the first forty zeros ξ_i of the function $J_0(\xi)$ with the corresponding values of $J_1(\xi_i)$ are available † so that it is convenient to express results of the kind (36.11) in terms of them. It is readily seen that in this case

$$\psi(\rho, z) = 8a^2 \psi_0 \sum_i \frac{e^{-\xi_i \zeta} J_0(\alpha \xi_i)}{\xi_i^3 J_1(\xi_1)} \qquad (36.12)$$

where $\zeta = z/a$ and $\alpha = \varrho/a$.

§ 37. Asymptotic expansions of Bessel functions.

In certain physical problems it is desirable to know the value of a Bessel function for large values of its argument. In this section we shall derive the asymptotic expansion of the Bessel function of the first kind $J_n(x)$ and merely indicate the results for the other Bessel occurring in mathematical physics.

We take equation (28.1) as our definition of the function $J_n(x)$. Applying the theory of functions of a complex variable it is readily shown that this definition is equivalent to

$$J_n(x) = \frac{(\frac{1}{2}x)^n}{\Gamma(\frac{1}{2})\Gamma(n+\frac{1}{2})} \left\{ \int_{L_1} (1-t^2)^{n-\frac{1}{2}} e^{ixt} dt + \int_{L_2} (1-t^2)^{n-\frac{1}{2}} e^{ixt} dt \right\} \qquad (37.1)$$

where L_1 is the straight line $\mathscr{R}(t) = -1$ in the upper half of complex t-plane and L_2 is the corresponding part of the straight line $\mathscr{R}(t) = +1$. By changing the variable

† A. Gray, G. B. Mathews and T. M. MacRobert, *A Treatise on Bessel Functions and Their Applications to Physics*, 2nd edition (Macmillan, 1931).

from t to $u = ix(1-t)$ in the first integral and to $u = -ix(1-t)$ in the second we see that

$$J_n(x) = \sqrt{\frac{2}{\pi x}} \{j_n(x) + j_n^*(x)\} \qquad (37.2)$$

where

$$j_n(x) = \frac{1}{2\Gamma(n+\frac{1}{2})} e^{ix-(\frac{1}{2}n+\frac{1}{4})\pi i} \int_0^\infty e^{-u} u^{n-\frac{1}{2}} \left(1 + \frac{iu}{2x}\right)^{n-\frac{1}{2}} du$$

and $j_n^*(x)$ denotes its complex conjugate. Expanding $(1+iu/2x)^{n-\frac{1}{2}}$ by the binomial theorem and integrating term by term we find that

$$j_n(x) = \frac{1}{2} e^{ix-(\frac{1}{2}n+\frac{1}{4})\pi i} {}_2F_0\left(\frac{1}{2}+n, \frac{1}{2}-n; \frac{1}{2ix}\right). \quad (37.3)$$

If we adopt Hankel's convention of writing

$$(n, r) = (-1)^r \frac{(\frac{1}{2}-n)_r(\frac{1}{2}+n)_r}{r!}$$

in equation (37.3) and substitute the result in equation (37.2) we find that for large values of x the asymptotic expansion of the Bessel function $J_n(x)$ is

$$J_n(x) \sim \sqrt{\frac{2}{\pi x}} \left\{ \cos(x-\tfrac{1}{2}n\pi-\tfrac{1}{4}\pi) \sum_{r=0}^\infty \frac{(-1)^r(n, 2r)}{(2x)^{2r}} \right.$$
$$\left. -\sin(x-\tfrac{1}{2}n\pi-\tfrac{1}{4}\pi) \sum_{r=0}^\infty \frac{(-1)^r(n, 2r+1)}{(2x)^{2r+1}} \right\}. \qquad (37.4)$$

The corresponding expansion for the Bessel function of the second kind is found to be

$$Y_n(x) \sim \sqrt{\frac{2}{\pi x}} \left\{ \sin(x-\tfrac{1}{2}n\pi-\tfrac{1}{4}\pi) \sum_{r=0}^\infty \frac{(-1)^r(n, 2r)}{(2x)^{2r}} \right.$$
$$\left. +\cos(x-\tfrac{1}{2}n\pi-\tfrac{1}{4}\pi) \sum_{r=0}^\infty \frac{(-1)^r(n, 2r+1)}{(2x)^{2r+1}} \right\}. \qquad (37.5)$$

Substituting these asymptotic expressions in equations (30.18) and (30.19) we find that as $x \to \infty$,

$$H_n^{(1)}(x) \sim \left(\frac{8}{\pi x}\right)^{\frac{1}{2}} j_n(x), \qquad H_n^{(2)}(x) \sim \left(\frac{8}{\pi x}\right)^{\frac{1}{2}} j_n^*(x) \quad (37.6)$$

where $j_n(x)$ is given by equation (37.3).

In certain problems only a very crude approximation to the behaviour of the Bessel function is desired. In these circumstances the following formulæ are usually sufficient:

$$J_n(x) \sim \sqrt{\frac{2}{\pi x}} \cos\left(x - \tfrac{1}{2}n\pi - \tfrac{1}{4}\pi\right),$$

$$Y_n(x) \sim \sqrt{\frac{2}{\pi x}} \sin\left(x - \tfrac{1}{2}n\pi - \tfrac{1}{4}\pi\right); \quad (37.7)$$

$$H_n^{(1)}(x) \sim \sqrt{\frac{2}{\pi x}} \, e^{ix - \frac{1}{2}n\pi i - \frac{1}{4}\pi i},$$

$$H_n^{(2)}(x) \sim \sqrt{\frac{2}{\pi x}} \, e^{-ix + \frac{1}{2}n\pi i - \frac{1}{4}\pi i}. \quad (37.8)$$

Similar formulæ exist for the modified Bessel functions. Proceeding in the same way as in the establishment of equation (28.1) we can show that

$$I_n(x) = \frac{1}{\sqrt{\pi}\,\Gamma(n + \tfrac{1}{2})} \left(\tfrac{1}{2}x\right)^n \int_{-1}^{1} e^{\pm xt}(1 - t^2)^{n - \frac{1}{2}}dt$$

which becomes

$$I_n(x) = \frac{1}{\sqrt{(2\pi x)}\,\Gamma(n + \tfrac{1}{2})} \left\{ e^{-x - (n + \frac{1}{2})\pi} \int_0^{\infty} e^{-u} u^{n - \frac{1}{2}} \left(1 + \frac{u}{2x}\right)^{n - \frac{1}{2}} du \right.$$

$$\left. + e^x \int_0^{\infty} e^{-u} u^{n - \frac{1}{2}} \left(1 - \frac{u}{2x}\right)^{n - \frac{1}{2}} du \right\}$$

by a simple change of variable. By a method similar to that employed above to obtain the asymptotic expansion of $J_n(x)$ we can then show that if $-\frac{1}{2}\pi < \arg x < \frac{3}{2}\pi$,

$$I_n(x) \sim \frac{1}{\sqrt{(2\pi x)}} e^x \sum_{r=0}^{\infty} \frac{(-1)^r (n, r)}{(2x)^r} + \frac{e^{-x+(n+\frac{1}{2})\pi i}}{\sqrt{(2\pi x)}} \sum_{r=0}^{\infty} \frac{(n, r)}{(2x)^r}$$

and that if $-\frac{3}{2}\pi < \arg x < \frac{1}{2}\pi$ the factor $\exp\{-x+(n+\frac{1}{2})\pi i\}$ is replaced by $\exp\{-x-(n+\frac{1}{2})\pi i\}$. The corresponding formula for the modified Bessel of the second kind is

$$K_n(x) \sim \left(\frac{\pi}{2x}\right)^{\frac{1}{2}} e^{-x} \sum_{r=0}^{\infty} \frac{(n, r)}{(2x)^r}$$

as $x \to \infty$.

Examples IV

(1) Making use of example 2 of Chapter II and of the expansion (25.8), expand $\cos(x \sin \theta)$ as a power series in $\sin \theta$ in two ways. Hence by equating powers of $\sin^{2s} \theta$ show that if s is a positive integer

$$x^{2s} = 2^{2s+1} \sum_{n=s}^{\infty} \frac{(n+s-1)!}{(n-s)!} J_{2n}(x).$$

Derive the corresponding result for x^{2s+1} and show that the two results may be combined into the single formula

$$x^r = 2^r \sum_{n=0}^{\infty} \frac{(r+n-1)!}{n!} (r+2n) J_{r+2n}(x)$$

$(r = 1, 2, 3, \ldots)$.

(2) If u and ζ denote the eccentric and mean anomalies of a planet show that

$$\cos(nu) = n \sum_{m=-\infty}^{\infty} \frac{1}{m} J_{m-n}(me) \cos(m\zeta),$$

$$\sin(nu) = n \sum_{m=-\infty}^{\infty} \frac{1}{m} J_{m-n}(me) \sin(m\zeta).$$

(3) Making use of the expression for $P_n(\cos\theta)$ given in example 19 of Chapter III show that

$$\sum_{n=0}^{\infty} \frac{r^n}{n!} P_n(\cos\theta) = e^{r\cos\theta} J_0(r\sin\theta).$$

(4) Show that

(i) $8J_n'''(z) = J_{n-3}(z) - 3J_{n-1}(z) + 3J_{n+1}(z) - J_{n+3}(z)$;

(ii) $4J_0'''(z) + 3J_0'(z) + J_3(z) = 0$.

(5) Prove that

$$\frac{1}{2} + \sum_{r=1}^{N} (-1)^r J_0(rx) = \frac{(-1)^N}{\pi} \int_0^x \frac{\cos(N+\frac{1}{2})u}{\cos\frac{1}{2}u} \frac{du}{\sqrt{(x^2-u^2)}}$$

and deduce that

$$\frac{1}{2} + \sum_{r=1}^{\infty} (-1)^r J_0(rx) = 0.$$

(6) Show that the curve with freedom equations

$$x = t - \sin t, \quad y = \cos t/(1-\cos t)$$

may be represented in the interval $0 < t < \pi$ by the Fourier series

$$y = 2\sum_{n=1}^{\infty} J_n(n)\cos(nx).$$

(7) Prove that

$$e^{ikr\cos\theta} = \left(\frac{\pi}{2kr}\right)^{\frac{1}{2}} \sum_{n=0}^{\infty} (2n+1)e^{\frac{1}{2}n\pi i} J_{n+\frac{1}{2}}(kr)P_n(\cos\theta).$$

(8) Prove that

$$\lim_{n\to\infty} P_n\left(\cos\frac{x}{n}\right) = J_0(x).$$

(9) Show that

(i) $\displaystyle\sum_{n=0}^{\infty} \frac{x^n}{n!} J_n(a) = J_0\{\sqrt{(a^2-2ax)}\};$

(ii) $\displaystyle\sum_{n=0}^{\infty} \frac{(-x)^n}{n!} a^{-\frac{1}{2}m-\frac{1}{2}n} J_{m+n}(2\sqrt{a}) = (x+a)^{-\frac{1}{2}m} J_m\{2\sqrt{(x+a)}\}.$

(10) Prove that if n is a positive integer

$$J_n(2\sqrt{x}) = (-1)^n x^{\frac{1}{2}n} \frac{d^n}{dx^n} J_0(2\sqrt{x}).$$

(11) If $x > a$ show that

$$\int_0^\pi e^{a\cos\theta} \cos(x\sin\theta)d\theta = J_0\{\sqrt{(x^2-a^2)}\}.$$

(12) Prove that, if $-1 < x < 1$,

$$\frac{1}{\sqrt{(1-x^2)}} = \tfrac{1}{2}\pi + \pi \sum_{m=1}^{\infty} J_0(m\pi)\cos(m\pi x).$$

Deduce that

$$J_0(x) = \frac{\sin x}{x}\left\{1 + 2x^2 \sum_{m=1}^{\infty} \frac{(-1)^m J_0(m\pi)}{x^2 - m^2\pi^2}\right\}.$$

(13) Prove that

$$J'_\nu(x)J_{-\nu}(x) - J_\nu(x)J'_{-\nu}(x) \equiv \frac{A}{x},$$

where A is a constant, and, by considering the series for $J_\nu(x)$ and $J_\nu(x)$ when x is small show that $A = (2/\pi)\sin(\nu\pi)$.

(14) Show that the complete solution of Bessel's equation may be written in the form

$$A J_n(x) + B J_n(x) \int^x \frac{d\xi}{\xi\{J_n(\xi)\}^2}.$$

where A and B are arbitrary constants.

(15) Show that the complete solution of the differential equation

$$\frac{d^2y}{dx^2} + \frac{1}{3}xy = 0$$

is

$$y = \sqrt{x}\{AJ_{\frac{1}{3}}(\xi) + BJ_{-\frac{1}{3}}(\xi)\},$$

where $\xi^2 = 4x^3/27$ and A and B are arbitrary constants.

(16) If a and b are real constants show that the roots of the equation

$$axJ_n'(x) + bJ_n(x) = 0$$

are simple roots except possibly the root $x = 0$.

Show also that the equations $J_n(x) = 0$, $J_n'(x) = 0$ have no roots in common except possibly $x = 0$.

(17) If $x > 1$ and $m + n + 1 > 0$, prove that

$$\int_0^\infty e^{-xt}I_{n+\frac{1}{2}}(t)t^{m-\frac{1}{2}}dt = \sqrt{\frac{2}{\pi}}(x^2-1)^{-\frac{1}{2}m}Q_n^m(x),$$

where $Q_n^m(x)$ denotes the associated Legendre function of the second kind.

(18) Prove that

$$I_n(x+y) = \sum_{m=0}^\infty I_m(x)I_{n-m}(y)$$

$$+ \sum_{m=1}^\infty \{I_m(x)I_{n+m}(y) + I_{n+m}(x)I_m(y)\}.$$

(19) Show that

$$\int_{-1}^1 e^{x\mu}P_n(\mu)d\mu = \sqrt{\frac{2\pi}{x}}I_{n+\frac{1}{2}}(x).$$

(20) Prove that

$$\sum_{n=-\infty}^\infty J_n(kx)t^n = e^{-\frac{x}{2t}\left(k-\frac{1}{k}\right)}\sum_{n=-\infty}^\infty k^n t^n J_n(x)$$

and deduce that

(i) $J_n(re^{i\theta}) = \sum_{m=0}^{\infty} J_{n+m}(r)e^{i(n+m)\theta} \dfrac{(-ir \sin \theta)^m}{m!};$

(ii) $I_n(x) = \sum_{m=0}^{\infty} \dfrac{x^m}{m!} J_{n+m}(x).$

(21) Using the expansion of the last question prove that $J_r(ae^{i\alpha} + be^{i\beta})$ is the coefficient of t^r in the expansion of

$$\exp\left\{-\frac{i(a \sin \alpha + b \sin \beta)}{t}\right\} \sum_{m=-\infty}^{\infty} \sum_{n=-\infty}^{\infty} e^{in\alpha - im\beta} J_n(a)J_m(b)t^{n+m}.$$

By putting $R = a \cos \alpha + b \cos \beta$, $0 = a \sin \alpha + b \sin \beta$, $\beta = \alpha + \theta - \pi$ prove Neumann's addition theorem

$$J_n(R) = \left(\frac{a - be^{-i\theta}}{a - be^{i\theta}}\right)^{\frac{1}{2}n} \sum_{m=-\infty}^{\infty} J_{n+m}(a)J_m(b)e^{-im\theta},$$

where $R^2 = a^2 + b^2 - 2ab \cos \theta$.

(22) Prove that

$$J_0(ax)J_0(bx) = \frac{1}{\pi} \int_0^{\pi} J_0(Rx)d\theta,$$

where $R^2 = a^2 + b^2 - 2ab \cos \theta$, and deduce that

$$\int_0^{\infty} J_0(ax)J_0(bx)e^{-cx}dx = \frac{k}{\pi\sqrt{(ab)}} K(k)$$

where

$$K(k) = \int_0^{\frac{1}{2}\pi} \frac{d\phi}{\sqrt{(1 - k^2 \sin^2 \phi)}}, \quad k^2 = \frac{4ab}{(a+b)^2 + c^2}.$$

Prove, in a similar way, that

$$\int_0^{\infty} J_1(ax)J_1(bx)e^{-cx}dx = \frac{2}{\pi k\sqrt{(ab)}} \left\{(1 - \tfrac{1}{2}k^2)K(k) - E(k)\right\}$$

where k and $K(k)$ are as defined above and

$$E(k) = \int_0^{\frac{1}{2}\pi} \sqrt{(1-k^2 \sin^2 \phi)}d\phi.$$

(23) Show that

$$J_m(x)J_n(x) = \frac{1}{\pi} e^{\frac{1}{2}(n-m)\pi i} \int_0^\pi J_{n-m}(2x \sin \theta)e^{(n+m)\theta i} \, d\theta$$

and hence that

$$\{J_n(x)\}^2 = \frac{1}{\pi} \int_0^\pi J_{2n}(2x \sin \theta)d\theta.$$

Deduce that

$$\{J_n(x)\}^2 = (\tfrac{1}{2}x)^{2n} \sum_{s=0}^\infty \frac{(2n+2s)!}{s!(2n+s)!(n+s)!} (-\tfrac{1}{4}x^2)^s.$$

(24) Prove that

$$\int_0^\infty J_0(ax)J_0(bx)e^{-p^2x^2}x\,dx = \frac{1}{2p} \exp\left(-\frac{a^2-b^2}{4p^2}\right) I_0\left(\frac{ab}{2p}\right).$$

(25) We define the **Bessel-integral function of order n** by the equation

$$Ji_n(x) = -\int_0^\infty \frac{J_n(u)}{u} \, du.$$

Prove that if n is even

$$Ji_n(x) = \frac{1}{\pi} \int_0^\pi \cos(n\theta)ci(x \sin \theta)d\theta,$$

where $ci(x)$ denotes the cosine integral, and derive the corresponding expression when n is odd.

Show that:

(i) $li\{e^{\frac{1}{2}x(t-1/t)}\} = \sum_{n=-\infty}^\infty t^n Ji_n(x);$

(ii) $Ji'_n(x) = J_n(x)/x;$

(iii) $(n-1)Ji_{n-1}(x)-(n+1)Ji_{n+1}(x) = 2nJi_n'(x)$;

(iv) $ci(x) = Ji_0(x) - 2Ji_2(x) + 2Ji_4(x) - \ldots$;

(v) $si(x) = 2Ji_1(x) - 2Ji_3(x) + 2Ji_5(x) - \ldots$;

(vi) $Ji_0(x) = \gamma + \log(\tfrac{1}{2}x) - \dfrac{x^2}{8}\, {}_2F_3(1, 1; 2, 2, 2; -x^2/4)$.

(26) If

$$I_m = \frac{1}{J_1(\lambda)} \int_0^1 x^{2m+1} J_0(\lambda x)\, dx$$

where λ is a zero of $J_0(x)$, show that

$$I_m = \frac{1}{\lambda}\left[1 - \frac{4m^2}{\lambda^2} + \frac{4^2 m^2(m-1)^2}{\lambda^4} \right.$$
$$\left. + \ldots + (-1)^m \frac{4^m m^2(m-1)^2 \ldots 2^2 . 1^2}{\lambda^{2m}} \right].$$

Show that

$$1 - x^{2m} = \sum_{i=1}^{\infty} a_i J_0(\lambda_i x), \quad 0 \leqq x \leqq 1,$$

where $\lambda_1, \lambda_2, \ldots$ are the positive zeros of $J_0(x)$ and

$$a_i = \frac{2}{J_1(\lambda_i)}(1 - I_m).$$

Putting $m = 1, 2, 3, \ldots$, and rearranging the series show that

$$\sum_{i=1}^{\infty} \frac{J_0(\lambda_i x)}{\lambda_i^3 J_1(\lambda_i)} = \frac{1}{8}(1-x)^2;$$

$$\sum_{i=1}^{\infty} \frac{J_0(\lambda_i x)}{\lambda_i^5 J_1(\lambda_i)} = \frac{1}{128}(1-x^2)(3-x^2);$$

$$\sum_{i=1}^{\infty} \frac{J_0(\lambda_i x)}{\lambda_i^7 J_1(\lambda_i)} = \frac{1}{4608}(1-x^2)(19-8x^2+x^4).$$

Deduce that

$$\sum_{i=1}^{\infty} \frac{1}{\lambda_i^3 J_1(\lambda_i)} = \frac{1}{8}; \quad \sum_{i=1}^{\infty} \frac{1}{\lambda_i^5 J_1(\lambda_i)} = \frac{3}{128}; \quad \sum_{i=1}^{\infty} \frac{1}{\lambda_i^7 J_1(\lambda_i)} = \frac{19}{4608}.$$

(27) If $\alpha_1, \alpha_2, \ldots$ denote the positive zeros of $J_\nu(x)$ show that

$$\sum_{i=1}^{\infty} \frac{1}{\alpha_i J_{\nu+1}(\alpha_i)} \int_0^1 x f(x) J_\nu(\alpha_i x) dx = \tfrac{1}{2} \int_0^1 x^{\nu+1} f(x) dx.$$

Taking $f(x) = x^\nu$, $x^{\nu+2}$ show that

$$\sum_{i=1}^{\infty} \frac{1}{\alpha_i^2} = \frac{1}{4(\nu+1)}; \quad \sum_{i=1}^{\infty} \frac{1}{\alpha_i^4} = \frac{1}{16(\nu+1)^2(\nu+2)}.$$

(28) Putting $\nu = 0$, $f(x) = x^m$ in (27), show that

$$\sum_{i=1}^{\infty} \frac{I_m}{\lambda_i} = \frac{1}{4(m+1)}$$

where $\lambda_1, \lambda_2, \ldots$ are the positive zeros of $J_0(x)$ and I_m is defined in (26).

Substituting the value for I_m derived in (26) and using the fact (obtained by putting $\nu = 0$ in (27)) that $\sum \lambda_i^{-2} = \tfrac{1}{4}$, show that the sum

$$S_{2m} = \sum_{i=1}^{\infty} \frac{1}{\lambda_i^{2m}}$$

satisfies the recurrence formula

$$S_{2m+2} = \sum_{r=1}^{m} (-1)^{m-r} \left(\frac{1}{4}\right)^{m-r+1} \frac{S_{2r}}{[(m-r+1)!]^2}$$
$$+ (-1)^m \left(\frac{1}{4}\right)^{m+1} \frac{1}{m!(m+1)!}.$$

Deduce that

$$\sum_{i=1}^{\infty} \frac{1}{\lambda_i^4} = \frac{1}{32}; \quad \sum_{i=1}^{\infty} \frac{1}{\lambda_i^6} = \frac{1}{192}; \quad \sum_{i=1}^{\infty} \frac{1}{\lambda_i^8} = \frac{11}{12288}.$$

(29) Show that

$$\sum_{i=1}^{\infty} \frac{J_0(\lambda_i x)}{\lambda_i^2 J_1^2(\lambda_i)} = -\tfrac{1}{2} \log x.$$

Multiplying both sides of this equation by x and integrating term by term, show that

$$\sum_{i=1}^{\infty} \frac{J_1(\lambda_i x)}{\lambda_i^3 J_1^2(\lambda_i)} = \tfrac{1}{8} x (1 - 2 \log x),$$

and hence that

$$\sum_{i=1}^{\infty} \frac{1}{\lambda_i^3 J_1(\lambda_i)} = \tfrac{1}{8}.$$

CHAPTER V

THE FUNCTIONS OF HERMITE AND LAGUERRE

§ 38. The Hermite polynomials. The Hermite polynomial $H_n(x)$ is defined for integral values of n and all real values of x by the identity

$$e^{2tx-t^2} = \sum_{n=0}^{\infty} \frac{H_n(x)}{n!} t^n. \tag{38.1}$$

If we write

$$f(x, t) = e^{2tx-t^2} = e^{x^2} e^{-(x-t)^2}$$

then it follows from Taylor's theorem that

$$H_n(x) = \left(\frac{\partial^n f}{\partial t^n}\right)_{t=0} = e^{x^2} \left[\frac{\partial^n}{\partial t^n} e^{-(x-t)^2}\right]_{t=0}$$

Now it is obvious from the form of the function $\exp\{-(x-t)^2\}$ that

$$\left[\frac{\partial^n}{\partial t^n} e^{-(x-t)^2}\right]_{t=0} = (-1)^n \frac{d^n}{dx^n}(e^{-x^2})$$

and so we have the form

$$H_n(x) = (-1)^n e^{x^2} \frac{d^n}{dx^n}(e^{-x^2}) \tag{38.2}$$

for the calculation of the polynomial $H_n(x)$.

It follows from this formula that the first eight Hermite polynomials are:

$H_0(x) = 1,$

$H_1(x) = 2x,$

$$H_2(x) = 4x^2 - 2,$$
$$H_3(x) = 8x^3 - 12x,$$
$$H_4(x) = 16x^4 - 48x^2 + 12,$$
$$H_5(x) = 32x^5 - 160x^3 + 120x,$$
$$H_6(x) = 64x^6 - 480x^4 + 720x^2 - 120,$$
$$H_7(x) = 128x^7 - 1344x^5 + 3360x^3 - 1680x.$$

In general we have

$$H_n(x) = (2x)^n - \frac{n(n-1)}{1!} (2x)^{n-2}$$
$$+ \frac{n(n-1)(n-3)(n-4)}{2!} (2x)^{n-4} + \dots$$

or, in the notation of Section 12,

$$H_n(x) = (2x)^n {}_2F_0\left(-\tfrac{1}{2}n, \tfrac{1}{2} - \tfrac{1}{2}n; -\frac{1}{x^2}\right). \qquad (38.3)$$

Recurrence formulæ for the Hermite polynomials follow directly from the defining relation (38.1). If we differentiate both sides of that equation with respect to x we obtain the relation

$$2te^{2xt-t^2} = \sum_{n=0}^{\infty} \frac{H_n'(x)}{n!} t^n$$

from which it follows directly that

$$2nH_{n-1}x = H_n'(x). \qquad (38.4)$$

On the other hand if we differentiate both sides of the identity (38.1) with respect to t we obtain the relation

$$2(x-t)e^{2tx-t^2} = \sum_{n=1}^{\infty} \frac{H_n(x)}{(n-1)!} t^{n-1}$$

which can be written in the form

$$2x \sum_{n=0}^{\infty} \frac{H_n(x)}{n!} t^n - 2 \sum_{n=0}^{\infty} \frac{H_n(x)}{n!} t^{n+1} = \sum_{n=1}^{\infty} \frac{H_n(x)}{(n-1)!} t^{n-1}$$

to yield the identity

$$2xH_n(x) = 2nH_{n-1}(x) + H_{n+1}(x) \qquad (38.5)$$

by the identification of coefficients of t^n.

Eliminating $2nH_{n-1}(x)$ from equations (38.4) and (38.5) we obtain the relation

$$H_n'(x) = 2xH_n(x) - H_{n+1}(x). \qquad (38.6)$$

Differentiating both sides of this identity we find that

$$H_n''(x) = 2xH_n'(x) + 2H_n(x) - H_{n+1}'(x)$$

and, by equation (38.4), $H_{n+1}'(x) = 2(n+1)H_n(x)$ so that

$$H_n''(x) - 2xH_n'(x) + 2nH_n(x) = 0. \qquad (38.7)$$

In other words $y = H_n(x)$ is a solution of the linear differential equation

$$y'' - 2xy' + 2ny = 0. \qquad (38.8)$$

§ 39. Hermite's differential equation. We saw in the last section that $H_n(x)$ is a solution of the differential equation (38.8). Replacing the integer n in that equation by the parameter v we obtain **Hermite's differential equation**

$$\frac{d^2y}{dx^2} - 2x\frac{dy}{dx} + 2vy = 0. \qquad (39.1)$$

If we assume a solution of this equation in the form

$$y = \sum_{r=0}^{\infty} a_r x^{r+\varrho}$$

and substitute in the equation (39.1) we obtain the recurrence relation

$$a_{r+2} = \frac{2(r+\varrho-v)}{(r+\varrho+2)(r+\varrho+1)} a_r \qquad (39.2)$$

on equating to zero the coefficient of $x^{r+\varrho}$. Equating to zero the coefficient of $x^{\varrho-2}$ we obtain the indicial equation

$$\varrho(\varrho-1) = 0. \qquad (39.3)$$

Corresponding to the root $\varrho = 0$ we have the recurrence relation

$$a_{r+2} = \frac{2(r-v)}{(r+1)(r+2)} a_r \qquad (39.4)$$

which gives the solution

$$y_1(x) = a_1\left(1 - \frac{2v}{2!}x^2 + \frac{2^2 v(v-2)}{4!}x^4 - \frac{2^3 v(v-2)(v-4)}{6!}x^6 + \ldots\right) \qquad (39.5)$$

where a_1 is a constant.

Similarly, corresponding to the root $\varrho = 1$ of the indicial equation we have the recurrence relation

$$a_{r+2} = \frac{2(r+1-v)}{(r+3)(r+2)} a_r \qquad (39.6)$$

from which is derived the solution

$$y_2(x) = a_2 x\left(1 - \frac{2(v-1)}{3!}x^2 + \frac{2^2(v-1)(v-3)}{5!}x^4 + \ldots\right) \qquad (39.7)$$

where a_2 is a constant. The general solution of Hermite's differential equation is therefore

$$y = y_1(x) + y_2(x). \qquad (39.8)$$

For general values of the parameter v the two series for $y_1(x)$ and $y_2(x)$ are infinite. From equations (39.4) and (39.6) it follows that for both series

$$a_{r+2} \sim \frac{2}{r} a_r, \quad \text{as } r \to \infty. \qquad (39.9)$$

If we write

$$\exp(x^2) = b_0 + b_2 x^2 + \ldots + b_r x^r + b_{r+2}x^{r+2} + \ldots$$

L

then

$$b_{r+2} \sim \frac{2}{r} b_r, \quad \text{as } r \to \infty. \tag{39.10}$$

Suppose that a_N/b_N is equal to a constant γ, which may be small or large, then it follows from equations (39.9) and (39.10) that, for large enough values of N, $a_{N+2m}/b_{N+2m} \sim \gamma$. In other words the higher terms of the series for $y_1(x)$, $y_2(x)$ differ from those of $\exp(x^2)$ only by multiplicative constants γ_1, γ_2, so that for large values of $|x|$,

$$y_1(x) \sim \gamma_1 e^{x^2}, \quad y_2(x) \sim \gamma_2 e^{x^2}$$

since for such values the lower terms are unimportant.

We shall see later (§ 41 below), that in quantum mechanics we require solutions of Hermite's differential equation which do not become infinite more rapidly than $\exp(\tfrac{1}{2}x^2)$ as $|x| \to \infty$. It follows from the above considerations that such solutions are possible only if either $y_1(x)$ or $y_2(x)$ reduce to simply polynomials and it is obvious from equations (39.5) and (39.7) that this occurs only if v is a positive integer. For example, if v is an *even* integer n we get the solution

$$y(x) = c H_n(x), \tag{39.11}$$

where c is a constant, by taking $a_2 = 0$,

$$a_1 = (-1)^{\frac{1}{2}n} \frac{n!}{(\tfrac{1}{2}n)!} c.$$

Similarly, if v is an *odd* integer n we get the solution (39.11) by taking $a_1 = 0$ and

$$a_2 = (-1)^{\frac{1}{2}n - \frac{1}{2}} \frac{2n!}{(\tfrac{1}{2}n - \tfrac{1}{2})!} c.$$

Hermite's differential equation therefore possesses solutions which do not become infinite more rapidly than $\exp(\tfrac{1}{2}x^2)$ as $|x| \to \infty$ if and only if v is a positive integer n. When this is so the required solution of Hermite's equation is given by equation (39.11).

§ 40. Hermite functions. A differential equation closely related to Hermite's equation is

$$\frac{d^2\psi}{dx^2} + (\lambda - x^2)\psi = 0. \tag{40.1}$$

If we transform the dependent variable from ψ to y where

$$\psi = e^{-\frac{1}{2}x^2}y \tag{40.2}$$

and put $\lambda = 1 + 2\nu$ then it is readily shown that y satisfies Hermite's equation (39.1). The general solution of equation (40.1) is therefore given by equations (40.2) and (39.8) with $y_1(x)$, $y_2(x)$ given by equations (39.5) and (39.7) respectively.

The argument at the end of the last section shows that the equation (40.1) possesses solutions which tend to zero as $|x| \to \infty$ if and only if the parameter λ is of the form $1 + 2n$ where n is a positive integer. When λ is of this form the required solution of (40.1) is a constant multiple of the function $\Psi_n(x)$ defined by the equation

$$\Psi_n(x) = e^{-\frac{1}{2}x^2}H_n(x) \tag{40.3}$$

where $H_n(x)$ is the Hermite polynomial of degree n. The function $\Psi_n(x)$ is called a **Hermite function of order n.**

The recurrence relations for $\Psi_n(x)$ follow immediately from those for $H_n(x)$. For instance equation (38.4) is equivalent to the relation

$$2n\Psi_{n-1}(x) = x\Psi_n(x) + \Psi'_n(x) \tag{40.4}$$

and equation (38.5) is unaltered in form so that

$$2x\Psi_n(x) = 2n\Psi_{n-1}(x) + \Psi_{n+1}(x). \tag{40.5}$$

Eliminating $2n\Psi_{n-1}(x)$ from equations (40.4) and (40.5) we have the relation

$$\Psi'_n(x) = x\Psi_n(x) - \Psi_{n+1}(x). \tag{40.6}$$

From the point of view of mathematical physics the

most important properties of Hermite functions concern integrals involving products of two of them. In establishing most of these properties the starting point is the observation that the function $\Psi_n(x)$ satisfies the relation

$$\Psi_n'' + (2n + 1 - x^2)\Psi_n = 0, \qquad (40.7)$$

as is obvious merely by substituting $2n + 1$ for λ in equation (40.1).

Writing down the corresponding relation for Ψ_m,

$$\Psi_m'' + (2m + 1 - x^2)\Psi_m = 0, \qquad (40.8)$$

multiplying it by Ψ_n and subtracting it from equation (40.7) multiplied by Ψ_m we obtain, as a result of integrating over $(-\infty, \infty)$, the relation

$$2(m - n) \int_{-\infty}^{\infty} \Psi_m \Psi_n dx = \int_{-\infty}^{\infty} (\Psi_m \Psi_n'' - \Psi_n \Psi_m'') dx.$$

Now an integration by parts shows that the right-hand side of this equation has the value

$$\left[\Psi_m \Psi_n' - \Psi_n \Psi_m' \right]_{-\infty}^{\infty} - \int_{-\infty}^{\infty} (\Psi_m' \Psi_n' - \Psi_n' \Psi_m') dx$$

and, if we remember that, for all positive integers n, $\Psi_n(x) \to 0$ as $|x| \to \infty$, we see that this has the value zero. Hence if we let

$$I_{m,n} = \int_{-\infty}^{\infty} \Psi_m(x) \Psi_n(x) dx$$

we see that

$$I_{m,n} = 0, \text{ if } m \neq n. \qquad (40.9)$$

In particular

$$I_{n-1, n+1} = 0$$

so that from equation (40.5) we have

$$\int_{-\infty}^{\infty} 2x \Psi_n(x) \Psi_{n-1}(x) dx = 2n I_{n-1, n-1}. \qquad (40.10)$$

Now if in equation (40.3) we substitute for $H_n(x)$ from equation (38.2) we have

$$\Psi_n(x) = (-1)^n e^{\frac{1}{2}x^2} \frac{d^n}{dx^n}(e^{-x^2}) \qquad (40.11)$$

so that the left-hand side of equation (40.10) is equal to

$$-\int_{-\infty}^{\infty} 2xe^{x^2} \frac{d^n}{dx^n}(e^{-x^2}) \frac{d^{n-1}}{dx^{n-1}}(e^{-x^2})dx$$

and an integration by parts shows that this is equal to

$$I_{n,\,n} + I_{n+1,\,n-1}$$

i.e. to $I_{n,\,n}$. Hence from equation (40.10) we have

$$I_{n,\,n} = 2nI_{n-1,\,n-1}.$$

Repeating this operation n times and noting that

$$I_{0,\,0} = \int_{-\infty}^{\infty} e^{-x^2}dx = \sqrt{\pi}$$

we find that

$$I_{n,\,n} = 2^n n! \sqrt{\pi}. \qquad (40.12)$$

Combining equations (40.9) and (40.12) we have finally

$$I_{m,\,n} = 2^n n! \sqrt{\pi} \delta_{mn}. \qquad (40.13)$$

The evaluation of more complicated integrals can be effected by combining this result with the recurrence formulæ we have already established for the Hermite functions. For instance, it follows from equation (40.5) that

$$\int_{-\infty}^{\infty} x\Psi_m(x)\Psi_n(x)dx = nI_{m,\,n-1} + \tfrac{1}{2}I_{m,\,n+1}$$

showing that

$$\int_{-\infty}^{\infty} x\Psi_m(x)\Psi_n(x)dx = 0 \text{ if } m \neq n \pm 1 \qquad (40.14)$$

and that

$$\int_{-\infty}^{\infty} x\Psi_n(x)\Psi_{n+1}(x)dx = 2^n(n+1)!\sqrt{\pi}. \qquad (40.15)$$

Similarly, making use of equation (40.4) and equations (40.13-15) we can show that

$$\int_{-\infty}^{\infty} \Psi_m(x)\Psi_n'(x)dx = \begin{cases} 0 \text{ if } m \neq n\pm 1 \\ 2^{n-1}n!\sqrt{\pi} \text{ if } m = n-1 \\ -2^n(n+1)!\sqrt{\pi} \text{ if } m = n+1. \end{cases}$$

§ 41. The occurrence of Hermite functions in wave mechanics.

The Hermite functions which we have discussed in the last section occur in the wave mechanical treatment of the harmonic oscillator.[†] Although this is a very simple mechanical system the analysis of its properties is of great importance because of its application to the quantum theory of radiation.

The Schrödinger equation corresponding to a harmonic oscillator of point mass m with vibrational frequency v is

$$\frac{d^2\psi}{dx^2} + \frac{8\pi^2 m}{h^2}(W - 2\pi^2 m v^2 x^2)\psi = 0, \qquad (41.1)$$

where W is the total energy of the oscillator and h is Planck's constant. The problem is to determine the wave functions ψ which have the property that

(i) $\psi \to 0$ as $|x| \to \infty$;

(ii) $\int_{-\infty}^{\infty} |\psi|^2 dx = 1$.

If we let

$$x = \frac{1}{2\pi}\sqrt{\frac{h}{mv}}\xi$$

[†] N. F. Mott and I. N. Sneddon, *Wave Mechanics and Its Applications* (Oxford, 1948), p. 50.

then the equation (41.1) becomes

$$\frac{d^2\psi}{d\xi^2} + \left(\frac{2W}{hv} - \xi^2\right)\psi = 0 \qquad (41.2)$$

and the conditions (i) and (ii) become

(i') $\psi \to 0$ as $|\xi| \to \infty$;

(ii') $\displaystyle\int_{-\infty}^{\infty} |\psi|^2 d\xi = 2\pi\sqrt{\frac{mv}{h}}.$

The argument given at the beginning of § 40 shows that equation (41.2) possesses solutions ψ which satisfy the condition (ii') if and only if the parameter $(2W/hv)$ which occurs in the equation takes one of the values $1 + 2n$ where n is a positive integer. In other words solutions of this type, which are known by the probability interpretation of the wave function ψ to correspond to stationary states of the system can exist if and only if

$$W = hv(n + \tfrac{1}{2}) \qquad (41.3)$$

where n is a positive integer. When this is the case the form of the wave function ψ is known from § 40 to be

$$\psi = C\Psi_n(\xi) \qquad (41.4)$$

where C is a constant. Applying condition (ii') and equation (40.12) we see that

$$C = \left(\frac{4\pi mv}{h}\right)^{\frac{1}{4}} \frac{1}{2^{\frac{1}{2}n}(n!)^{\frac{1}{2}}}.$$

Thus the wave function corresponding to an admissible energy $(n + \tfrac{1}{2})hv$ is

$$\psi_n = \left(\frac{4\pi mv}{h}\right)^{\frac{1}{4}} \frac{\Psi_n(\xi)}{2^{\frac{1}{2}n}(n!)^{\frac{1}{2}}}, \quad \xi = 2\pi\sqrt{\frac{mv}{h}}\,x. \qquad (41.6)$$

In quantum theory the matrix elements $(n \mid x \mid p)$

defined by the equation

$$(n \mid x \mid p) = \int_{-\infty}^{\infty} x\psi_n(x)\psi_p(x)dx$$

are of considerable importance in the case of the harmonic oscillator. In terms of the variable ξ we have

$$(n \mid x \mid p) = \frac{h}{4\pi^2 mv} \int_{-\infty}^{\infty} \xi\psi_n(\xi)\psi_p(\xi)d\xi,$$

so that substituting from equation (41.6) we have

$$(n \mid x \mid p) = \frac{1}{\pi}\sqrt{\frac{h}{4\pi mv}} \int_{-\infty}^{\infty} \xi\Psi_n(\xi)\Psi_p(\xi)d\xi \div \{2^{\frac{1}{2}n+\frac{1}{2}p}(n!)^{\frac{1}{2}}(p!)^{\frac{1}{2}}\}.$$

It follows then from equations (40.14) and (40.15) that

$$(n \mid x \mid p) = 0 \quad \text{if } p \neq n \pm 1 \tag{41.7}$$

and that

$$(n \mid x \mid n+1) = \left\{\frac{(n+1)h}{8\pi^2 mv}\right\}^{\frac{1}{2}}, \tag{41.8}$$

$$(n \mid x \mid n-1) = \left\{\frac{nh}{8\pi^2 mv}\right\}^{\frac{1}{2}}. \tag{41.9}$$

§ 42. The Laguerre polynomials.

The **Laguerre polynomials** $L_n(x)$ are defined for n a positive integer and x a positive real number by the equation

$$\exp\left(-\frac{xt}{1-t}\right) = (1-t) \sum_{n=0}^{\infty} \frac{L_n(x)}{n!} t^n. \tag{42.1}$$

Expanding the exponential function we see that

$$(1-t)^{-1}\exp\left(-\frac{xt}{1-t}\right) = \sum_{r=0}^{\infty} \frac{(-1)^r x^r t^r}{r!(1-t)^{r+1}}$$

$$= \sum_{r=0}^{\infty} \sum_{s=0}^{\infty} \frac{(-1)^r(r+1)s}{r!s!} x^r t^{r+s}.$$

The coefficient of t^n in this expansion is

$$\sum_{r=0}^{n} \frac{(-1)^r (r+1)_{n-r}}{r!(n-r)!} x^r.$$

Using the relations

$$(r+1)_{n-r} = \frac{n!}{r!}, \quad \frac{(-1)^r}{(n-r)!} = \frac{(-n)r}{n!}$$

we see that this sum can be written in the form

$$\sum_{r=0}^{n} \frac{(-n)_r}{(r!)^2} x^r.$$

Identifying the coefficient of t^n with $L_n(x)/n!$ and adopting the notation of § 11 we see that

$$L_n(x) = n! \, _1F_1(-n; 1; x). \qquad (42.2)$$

It should be observed that $L_n(x)$ is a polynomial of degree n in x, and that the coefficient of x^n is $(-1)^n$.

A useful formula for the polynomial $L_n(x)$ can be obtained by finding a new representation for the confluent hypergeometric function on the right-hand side of equation (42.2). By Leibnitz's theorem for the nth derivative of a product of two functions we have

$$e^x D^n(x^n e^{-x}) = e^x \sum_{r=0}^{n} (-1)^r \frac{(-n)_r}{r!} (D^{n-r} x^n)(D^r e^{-x})$$

where D denotes the operator d/dx. Using the relations

$$e^x D^r(e^{-x}) = (-1)^r, \quad D^{n-r} x^n = n! x^r / r!$$

we see that

$$e^x D^n(x^n e^{-x}) = n! \sum_{r=0}^{n} \frac{(-n)^r}{(r!)^2} (x)^r. \qquad (42.3)$$

It follows immediately from equation (42.2) that

$$L_n(x) = e^x \frac{d^n}{dx^n} (x^n e^{-x}). \qquad (42.4)$$

The first five Laguerre polynomials can be calculated easily from this equation; we find that

$$L_0(x) = 1,$$
$$L_1(x) = 1-x,$$
$$L_2(x) = 2-4x+x^2,$$
$$L_3(x) = 6-18x+9x^2-x^3,$$
$$L_4(x) = 24-96x+72x^2-16x^3+x^4.$$

Equations (42.4) can be used to show that the functions

$$\phi_n(x) = \frac{1}{n!} e^{-\frac{1}{2}x} L_n(x) \tag{42.5}$$

form an orthonormal system. From (42.4) we have as a result of m integrations by parts

$$\int_0^\infty e^{-x} x^m L_n(x) dx = \int_0^\infty x^m \frac{d^n}{dx^n}(x^n e^{-x}) dx$$

$$= (-1)^m m! \int_0^\infty \frac{d^{n-m}}{dx^{n-m}}(x^n e^{-x}) dx$$

and this is zero if $n>m$. Since $L_m(x)$ is a polynomial of degree m in x it follows that

$$\int_0^\infty e^{-x} L_m(x) L_n(x) dx = 0 \text{ if } m \neq n. \tag{42.6}$$

Since the term of degree n in $L_n(x)$ is $(-1)^n x^n$ it follows that, when $m = n$,

$$\int_0^\infty e^{-x}\{L_n(x)\}^2 dx = (-1)^n \int_0^\infty e^{-x} x^n L_n(x) dx$$

$$= \int_0^\infty n! x^n e^{-x} dx$$

$$= (n!)^2$$

Combining this result with equation (42.6) we find that

$$\int_0^\infty e^{-x}\phi_m(x)\phi_n(x)dx = \delta_{mn}, \qquad (42.7)$$

showing that the ϕ's form an orthonormal set.

Recurrence formulæ for the Laguerre polynomials may be derived directly from the definition (42.1). Differentiating both sides of this equation with respect to t we obtain the identity

$$-\frac{x}{(1-t)^2} \cdot \exp\left(-\frac{xt}{1-t}\right)$$
$$= (1-t)\sum_{n=0}^\infty \frac{L_n(x)t^{n-1}}{(n-1)!} - \sum_{n=0}^\infty \frac{L_n(x)t^n}{n!}$$

which may be written in the form

$$x\sum_{n=0}^\infty \frac{L_n(x)t^n}{n!} + (1-t)^2\sum_{n=0}^\infty \frac{L_n(x)t^{n-1}}{(n-1)!}$$
$$-(1-t)\sum_{n=0}^\infty \frac{L_n(x)t^n}{n!} = 0.$$

Equating to zero the coefficient of t^n in the expansion on the left we obtain the recurrence relation

$$L_{n+1}(x)+(x-2n-1)L_n(x)+n^2L_{n-1}(x) = 0. \quad (42.8)$$

Similarly if we differentiate both sides of (42.1) with respect to x we obtain the identity

$$t\sum_{n=0}^\infty \frac{L_n(x)}{n!}t^n + (1-t)\sum_{n=0}^\infty \frac{L_n'(x)}{n!}t^n = 0$$

which yields the recurrence relation

$$L_n'(x) - nL_{n-1}'(x) + nL_{n-1}(x) = 0. \qquad (42.9)$$

Differentiating equation (42.8) twice with respect to x and replacing n by $n+1$ we find that

$$L''_{n+2}(x) + (x-2n-3)L''_{n+1}(x)$$
$$+(n+1)^2 L''_n(x) + 2L'_{n+1}(x) = 0. \qquad (42.10)$$

Now from (42.9)

$$L'_{n+1}(x) = (n+1)\{L'_n(x) - L_n(x)\},$$

and hence

$$L''_{n+1}(x) = (n+1)\{L''_n(x) - L'_n(x)\}.$$

A similar expression for $L''_{n+2}(x)$ in terms of $L_n(x)$ and its derivatives can be readily obtained. Substituting these values of $L''_{n+1}(x)$ and $L'_{n+1}(x)$ in equation (42.10) we find that

$$xL''_n(x) + (1-x)L'_n(x) + nL_n(x) = 0. \qquad (42.11)$$

§43. Laguerre's differential equation.

Equation (42.8) shows that $y = AL_n(x)$ is a solution of **Laguerre's differential equation**

$$x\frac{d^2y}{dx^2} + (1-x)\frac{dy}{dx} + vy = 0 \qquad (43.1)$$

in the case in which v is a positive integer n. If we put $\gamma = 1$, $\alpha = -v$ in equation (11.2) we see that it takes the form (43.1) so that it follows from equation (11.4) that one solution of equation (43.1) is

$$y_1(x) = {}_1F_1(-v; 1; x), \qquad (43.2)$$

Similarly we see from equation (11.8) that the second solution is

$$y_2(x) = y_1(x) . \log x + \sum_{r=1}^{\infty} c_r x^r \qquad (43.3)$$

where the coefficients c_r are defined by equations of the type (11.9). The general solution of Laguerre's differential equation may therefore be written in the form

$$y = Ay_1(x) + By_2(x)$$

where A and B are constants and $y_1(x)$, $y_2(x)$ are defined by equations (43.2) and (43.3) respectively.

If we are interested only in solutions which remain finite at $x = 0$ it is obvious from equation (43.3) that we must take the constant B to be zero. Further if a_r is the coefficient of x^r in the series expansion for $y_1(x)$ it is easily shown that $a_{r+1}/a_r \sim r^{-1}$. As the result of a discussion similar to that advanced in § 39, it follows that if v is not an integer

$$y_1(x) \sim e^x \text{ as } x \to \infty.$$

If, therefore, we are looking for solutions which increase less rapidly than this we must take v to a positive integer, in which case $y_1(x)$ reduces to a polynomial.

The equation (43.1) possesses a solution which increases less rapidly than e^x as $x \to \infty$ if and only if the parameter v occurring in it is a positive integer, n say. If it is also required that the solution shall remain finite at $x = 0$, the solution is of the form

$$y = AL_n(x) \tag{43.4}$$

where A is a constant and $L_n(x)$ is the Laguerre polynomial of degree n.

§ 44. The associated Laguerre polynomials and functions.

If we differentiate Laguerre's differential equation m times with respect to x we find that it becomes

$$x \frac{d^{m+2}y}{dx^{m+2}} + (m+1-x) \frac{d^{m+1}y}{dx^{m+1}} + (n-m) \frac{d^m y}{dx^m} = 0,$$

which shows that $L_n^m(x)$ defined by

$$L_n^m(x) = \frac{d^m}{dx^m} L_n(x), \quad (n \geqq m) \tag{44.1}$$

is a solution of the differential equation

$$x \frac{d^2 y}{dx^2} + (m+1-x) \frac{dy}{dx} + (n-m)y = 0. \tag{44.2}$$

The polynomial $L_n^m(x)$ defined by equation (44.1) is called the **associated Laguerre polynomial.** It follows from equation (42.2) that it may be presented as a series by the equation

$$L_n^m(x) = \frac{(-1)^m (n!)^2}{m!(n-m)!} \,_1F_1(-n+m; \; m+1; \; x) \quad (n \geqq m). \quad (44.3)$$

Similarly equation (42.4) leads to the formula

$$L_n^m(x) = \frac{d^m}{dx^m} \left\{ e^x \frac{d^n}{dx^n} (x^n e^{-x}) \right\}. \quad (44.4)$$

The simplest associated Laguerre polynomials are:

$L_1^1(x) = -1$,

$L_2^1(x) = -4 + 2x, \quad L_2^2(x) = 2$,

$L_3^1(x) = -18 + 18x - 3x^2, \quad L_3^2(x) = 18 - 6x, \quad L_3^3(x) = -6$,

$L_4^1(x) = -96 + 144x - 48x^2 + 4x^3, \quad L_4^2(x) = 144 - 96x + 12x^2$

$L_4^3(x) = -96 + 24x, \quad L_4^4(x) = 24$.

The definition (44.1) for the associated Laguerre polynomial is the one usually taken in applied mathematics. In pure mathematics the function

$$L_n^{(m)}(x) = \frac{(m+n)!}{m!n!} \,_1F_1(-n; \; m+1; \; x) \quad (44.5)$$

which is a solution of the differential equation

$$x \frac{d^2 y}{dx^2} + (m+1-x) \frac{dx}{dy} + ny = 0$$

is often taken as the definition of the associated Laguerre polynomial † so that care must be taken in reading the

† See, for instance, E. T. Copson, *Functions of a Complex Variable* (Oxford University Press, 1935), p. 269.

literature to ensure that the particular convention being followed is understood.

It is readily shown from equation (42.1) which defines the generating function for Laguerre polynomials that the associated Laguerre polynomials may be defined by the equation

$$(-1)^m t^m \exp\left(-\frac{xt}{1-t}\right) = (1-t)^{m+1} \sum_{n=m}^{\infty} \frac{L_n^m(x)}{n!} t^n. \quad (44.6)$$

This identity can then be used to derive recurrence relations for the associated Laguerre polynomials similar to those of equations (42.8) and (42.9) (cf. examples 6 (ii), (iii) below).

The **Laguerre functions** $R_{nl}(x)$ are defined by the equation

$$R_{nl}(x) = e^{-\frac{1}{2}x} x^l L_{n+1}^{2l+1}(x) \quad (n \geq l+1). \quad (44.7)$$

If in equation (44.2) we replace m by $2l+1$, n by $n+1$ and y by $e^{\frac{1}{2}x} x^{-1} R$ we see that the function $R_{nl}(x)$ is a solution of the ordinary linear differential equation

$$\frac{d^2 R}{dx^2} + \frac{2}{x}\frac{dR}{dx} - \left\{\frac{1}{4} - \frac{n}{x} + \frac{l(l+1)}{x^2}\right\} R = 0. \quad (44.8)$$

In most physical problems in which this equation arises it is known that l is an integer. By reasoning similar to that outlined in § 43 it can readily be shown that the equation (44.8) possesses a solution which is finite at $x = 0$ and tends to zero as $x \to \infty$ if, and only if, the parameter n which occurs in it assumes integral values. When this does occur the solution is $AR_{nl}(x)$ where the function $R_{nl}(x)$ is given by equation (44.7) and A is an arbitrary constant.

We shall now evaluate the integral

$$I_{nl} = \int_0^{\infty} x^2 \{R_{nl}(x)\}^2 dx$$

which arises in wave mechanics. From equation (44.6) we

have the identity

$$\sum_{n=l+1}^{\infty} \sum_{n'=l+1}^{\infty} \frac{L_{n+l}^{2l+1}(x)L_{n'+l}^{2l+1}(x)}{(n+l)!(n'+l)!} t^{n+l}\tau^{n'+l}$$

$$= \frac{\exp\left\{-\frac{xt}{1-t} - \frac{x\tau}{1-\tau}\right\}}{(1-t)^{2l+2}(1-\tau)^{2l+2}} t^{2l+1}\tau^{2l+1}$$

from which it follows that

$$\sum_{n=l+1}^{\infty} \sum_{n'=l+1}^{\infty} \frac{t^{n+l}\tau^{n'+l}}{(n+l)!(n'+l)!} \int_{0}^{\infty} e^{-x}x^{2l+2}L_{n+l}^{2l+1}(x)L_{n'+l}^{2l+1}(x)dx$$

$$= \frac{(t\tau)^{2l+1}}{(1-t)^{2l+2}(1-\tau)^{2l+2}} \int_{0}^{\infty} x^{2l+2}\exp\left\{-x - \frac{xt}{1-t} - \frac{x\tau}{1-\tau}\right\} dx.$$

This last integration is elementary and gives for the expression on the right

$$\frac{(2l+2)!(t\tau)^{2l+1}(1-t)(1-\tau)}{(1-t\tau)^{2l+3}}$$

and by means of the binomial theorem we may expand this function in the form

$$(1-t-\tau-t\tau) \sum_{r=0}^{\infty} \frac{(2l+r+2)!}{r!} (t\tau)^{2l+r+1}.$$

Now the coefficient of $(t\tau)^{n+1}$ in this expansion is

$$\frac{2n\{(n+l)!\}}{(n-l-1)!}$$

and this is equal to $I_{nl}/\{(n+l)!\}^2$. Hence

$$\int_{0}^{\infty} x^2\{R_{nl}(x)\}^2 dx = \frac{2n\{(n+l)!\}^3}{(n-l-1)!}. \tag{44.9}$$

§ 45. The wave functions for the hydrogen atom.

We shall conclude this chapter by discussing the motion of a single electron of mass m and charge $-e$ in the Coulomb field of force with potential

$$V(r) = - \frac{Ze^2}{r},$$

due to a nucleus of charge Ze. In a first approximation we may treat the mass of the nucleus as infinite and in this case the wave function ψ of the system is governed by the Schrödinger equation

$$\nabla^2 \psi + \frac{8\pi^2 m}{h^2}\left(W + \frac{Ze^2}{r}\right)\psi = 0 \qquad (45.1)$$

and the conditions:

(i) $\psi(r, \theta, \phi + 2\pi) = \psi(r, \theta, \phi)$ for all r, θ, ϕ;

(ii) ψ must be bounded in the range $0 \leq \theta \leq \pi$ for all r, ϕ;

(iii) $\psi \to 0$ as $r \to \infty$;

(iv) ψ remains finite as $r \to 0$;

(v) ψ is normalised to unity, i.e. $\int |\psi|^2 d\tau = 1$ where the integral is taken throughout the whole of space.

W is the total energy of the system.

The equation (45.1) may be solved by setting

$$\psi = R(r)\Theta(\theta)\Phi(\phi), \qquad (45.2)$$

where, by the method of separation of variables we have

$$\frac{d^2\Phi}{d\phi^2} + u^2\Phi = 0, \qquad (45.3)$$

$$\frac{1}{\sin\theta}\frac{d}{d\theta}\left(\sin\theta\frac{d\Theta}{d\theta}\right) + \left\{l(l+1) - \frac{u^2}{\sin^2\theta}\right\}\Theta = 0, \quad (45.4)$$

M

$$\frac{1}{r^2}\frac{d}{dr}\left(r^2\frac{dR}{dr}\right) + \left\{\frac{8\pi^2 m}{h^2}\left(W + \frac{Ze^2}{r}\right) - \frac{l(l+1)}{r^2}\right\} R = 0. \quad (45.5)$$

To satisfy condition (i) we must choose as a solution of (45.3) a function $\Phi(\phi)$ such that $\Phi(\phi+2\pi) = \Phi(\phi)$ for all ϕ. Thus u occurring in equation (45.3) must be an integer and a convenient solution will be

$$\Theta = Ae^{iu\phi} \quad (45.6)$$

where A is an arbitrary constant. Equation (45.5) is the well-known equation of which the solution is the associated Legendre polynomial $P_l^u(\cos\theta)$. If l is integral and $l \geqq |u|$, then $P_l^u(\cos\theta)$ is the only solution which is bounded in the range $0 \leqq \theta \leqq \pi$ and is therefore the only one leading to a wave function ψ which satisfies condition (ii) above; if l is not an integer no bounded solution exists.

To solve equation (45.5) we write

$$\alpha^2 = -\frac{8\pi^2 mW}{h^2}, \quad v = \frac{4\pi^2 mZe^2}{h^2\alpha} \quad (45.7)$$

and change the independent variable from r to x where $x = 2\alpha r$. We then find that

$$\frac{d^2R}{dx^2} + \frac{2}{x}\frac{dR}{dx} - \left\{\frac{1}{4} - \frac{v}{x} + \frac{l(l+1)}{x^2}\right\} R = 0 \quad (45.8)$$

where, in order that conditions (iii) and (iv) should be satisfied, R must be such that $R \to 0$, as $x \to \infty$ and as $x \to 0$. From the arguments of § 44 it follows that this is possible only if l is a positive integer and only if v is an integer, n say, which is greater than $l+1$. When this is so we may write the solution of equation (45.8) in the form (44.7) so that the solution of (45.5) is proportional to $R_{nl}(2\alpha r)$. Now by the second of the equations (45.7) we have

$$W = -\frac{2\pi^2 Z^2 e^4 m}{h^2 n^2} \quad (45.9)$$

for the possible values of the total energy W. The wave functions corresponding to the value of energy given by the integer n are

$$\psi_{nlu}(r, \theta, \phi) = C_{nlu}R_{nl}(2\alpha r)P_l^u(\cos \theta)e^{iu\phi} \qquad (45.10)$$

where C_{nlu} is a constant determined by the condition (v). In polar coordinates $d\tau = r^2 \sin \theta \, dr d\theta \, d\phi$ so that this condition gives

$$1 = C_{nlu}^2 \int_0^{2\pi} d\phi \int_0^{\pi} \sin \theta \{P_l^u(\cos \theta)\}^2 d\theta \int_0^{\infty} r^2 R_{nl}^2(2\alpha r)dr$$

so that it follows from equations (21.20) and (44.9) that

$$C_{nlu} = (2\alpha)^{\frac{3}{2}} \left\{ \frac{(-1)^u(l-u)!(n-l-1)!(2l+1)}{8\pi u(l+u)!\{(n+l)!\}^3} \right\}^{\frac{1}{2}}. \qquad (45.11)$$

Now from equations (45.7) and (45.9) we find that $\alpha = 4\pi^2 Ze^2 m/(h^2 n)$ so that if we introduce the Bohr radius a by means of the equation

$$a = \frac{h^2}{4\pi^2 me^2} \qquad (45.12)$$

we find that $\alpha = Z/an$. Introducing this result into (45.11) and substituting the value obtained for C_{nlu} into equation (45.10) we find that

$$\psi_{nlu}(r, \theta, \phi)$$
$$\left\{ \left(\frac{2Z}{an}\right)^3 \cdot \frac{(l-u)!(n-l-1)!(2l+1)}{(l+u)!\{(n+l)!\}^3 8\pi n} \right\}^{\frac{1}{2}} R_{nl}(2\alpha r)P_l^n(\cos \theta)e^{iu\phi}$$
$$(45.13)$$

with $u \leq l \leq n-1$ are the wave-functions corresponding to the energy (45.9) of the hydrogen atom.

If we write $W_0 = -2\pi^2 Z^2 e^4 m/h^2$ then corresponding to the energy W_0 we have the wave function

$$\psi_{100}(r, \theta, \phi) = \frac{1}{\sqrt{\pi}} \left(\frac{Z}{a}\right)^{\frac{3}{2}} e^{-\varrho} \quad (\varrho = Zr/a),$$

and to the energy level $W_0/4$ we have the three wave functions

$$\psi_{200}(r, \theta, \phi) = \frac{1}{4\sqrt{(2\pi)}} \left(\frac{Z}{a}\right)^{\frac{3}{2}} (2-\varrho)e^{-\frac{1}{2}\varrho},$$

$$\psi_{210}(r, \theta, \psi) = \frac{1}{4\sqrt{(2\pi)}} \left(\frac{Z}{a}\right)^{\frac{3}{2}} \varrho e^{-\frac{1}{2}\varrho} \cos\theta,$$

$$\psi_{211}(r, \theta, \phi) = \frac{1}{8\sqrt{(\pi)}} \left(\frac{Z}{a}\right)^{\frac{3}{2}} \varrho e^{-\frac{1}{2}\varrho} \sin\theta e^{\pm i\phi}.$$

From the last of these functions we can construct two functions

$$\frac{1}{4\sqrt{2\pi}} \left(\frac{Z}{a}\right)^{\frac{3}{2}} \varrho e^{-\frac{1}{2}\varrho} \sin\theta \frac{\sin}{\cos} \phi.$$

Similarly corresponding to the energy $W_0/9$ we have the six wave functions

$$\psi_{300}(r, \theta, \phi) = \frac{1}{81\sqrt{3\pi}} \left(\frac{Z}{a}\right)^{\frac{3}{2}} (27-18\varrho+2\varrho^2)e^{-\frac{1}{3}\varrho},$$

$$\psi_{310}(r, \theta, \phi) = \frac{\sqrt{2}}{81\sqrt{\pi}} \left(\frac{Z}{a}\right)^{\frac{3}{2}} (6-\varrho)\varrho e^{-\frac{1}{3}\varrho} \cos\theta,$$

$$\psi_{311}(r, \theta, \phi) = \frac{1}{81\sqrt{\pi}} \left(\frac{Z}{a}\right)^{\frac{3}{2}} (6-\varrho)\varrho e^{-\frac{1}{3}\varrho} \sin\theta e^{\pm i\phi},$$

$$\psi_{320}(r, \theta, \phi) = \frac{1}{81\sqrt{6\pi}} \left(\frac{Z}{a}\right)^{\frac{3}{2}} \varrho^2 e^{-\frac{1}{3}\varrho}(3\cos^2\theta-1),$$

$$\psi_{321}(r, \theta, \phi) = \frac{1}{81\sqrt{\pi}} \left(\frac{Z}{a}\right)^{\frac{3}{2}} \varrho^2 e^{-\frac{1}{3}\varrho} \sin\theta\cos\theta e^{\pm i\phi},$$

$$\psi_{322}(r, \theta, \phi) = \frac{1}{162\sqrt{\pi}} \left(\frac{Z}{a}\right)^{\frac{3}{2}} \varrho^2 e^{-\frac{1}{3}\varrho} \sin^2\theta e^{\pm 2i\phi}.$$

In wave mechanics $\left| \psi(r, \theta, \phi) \right|^2 d\tau$ represents the probability that the electron whose wave-function is $\psi(r, \theta, \phi)$ is to be found in a small volume $d\tau$ centred at the point whose polar coordinates are (r, θ, ϕ). To make the total probability unity we must have

$$\int \left| \psi(r, \theta, \phi) \right|^2 d\tau = 1,$$

where the integral is taken throughout the whole space. Since, in polar coordinates, $d\tau = r^2 \sin \theta \, dr d\theta \, d\phi$ it follows that the probability that the electron is at a distance between $r - \tfrac{1}{2}dr$ and $r + \tfrac{1}{2}dr$ from the nucleus is $\phi(r)dr$ where

$$\phi(r) = r^2 \int_0^{2\pi} d\phi \int_0^{\pi} \sin \theta \, d\theta \, . \, \left| \psi(r, \theta, \phi) \right|^2.$$

Hence for an electron in the state defined by quantum numbers n, l, u (equation (45.13) above) we have

$$\phi(r) \equiv \left(\frac{2Z}{an} \right)^3 \frac{(n-l-1)!}{2n\{(n+i)!\}^3} \, r^2 \{R_{nl}(2\alpha r)\}^2.$$

The mean value of any function f which depends on r alone is given by

$$\bar{f} = \int_0^{\infty} f(r)\phi(r)dr,$$

that is, by the formula

$$\bar{f} = \left(\frac{2Z}{an} \right)^3 \frac{(n-l-1)!}{2n\{(n+l)!\}^3} \int_0^{\infty} r^2 f(r)\{R_n(2\alpha r)\}^2 dr.$$

For examples of the use of this formula see example 17, p. 178.

Examples V

(1) Prove that if $m < n$

$$\frac{d^m}{dx^m}\{H_n(x)\} = \frac{2^m n!}{(n-m)!}\,H_{n-m}(x).$$

(2) If

$$K(x, y, t) = \sum_{n=0}^{\infty} \psi_n(x)\psi_n(y)t^n,$$

where the $\psi_n(x)$ are the orthonormal set of Hermite functions defined by the relation

$$\psi_n(x) + 2^{-\frac{1}{2}n}(n!)^{-\frac{1}{2}}\pi^{-\frac{1}{4}}\Psi_n(x),$$

prove that

$$\int_{-\infty}^{\infty} e^{-\frac{1}{2}x^2 + 2\lambda x - \lambda^2}K(x, y, t)dx = e^{-\frac{1}{2}y^2 + 2\lambda ty - \lambda^2 t^2}.$$

Assuming that $K(x, y, t)$ is of the form

$$A \exp (Bx^2 + Cxy + Dy^2)$$

where A, B, C and D are functions of t prove that

$$K(x, y, t) = \frac{1}{\sqrt{\{\pi(1-t)^2)\}}}\exp\left\{\frac{4xyt - (x^2 + y^2)(1 + t^2)}{2(1-t)^2}\right\}.$$

(3) Show that

$$\sum_{n=0}^{\infty}\{H_n(x)\}^2\,\frac{t^n}{n!} = \frac{1}{\sqrt{(1-4t^2)}}\exp\left\{\frac{4x^2 t}{1+t}\right\}.$$

(4) The Schrödinger equation for the three-dimensional oscillator in cylindrical coordinates (ϱ, ϕ, z) is

$$\nabla^2\psi + \frac{8\pi^2 m}{h^2}\{W - 2\pi^2 m(v^2\varrho^2 + \omega^2 z^2)\}\psi = 0.$$

Show that the solutions ψ of this equation such that

$\psi \to 0$ as ϱ and $z \to \infty$ and ψ is finite at the origin are of the form

$$C \exp\{ iu - \tfrac{1}{2}\alpha^2\varrho^2 - \tfrac{1}{2}\beta^2 z^2\} f_{l|u|}(\xi) H_n(z),$$

where C is a constant, l, n, $|u|$ are positive integers, $\alpha = 2\pi\sqrt{(mv/h)}$, $\beta = 2\pi\sqrt{(m\omega/h)}$, and $f_{l|u|}(\xi)$ is a polynomial of degree $2l$ in ξ which satisfies the equation

$$\frac{d^2f}{d\xi^2} - \left(2\xi - \frac{1}{\xi}\right)\frac{df}{d\xi} + \left(2|u| + 2l - \frac{u^2}{\xi^2}\right)f = 0.$$

Show also that the corresponding values of W are given by the equation

$$W = (2l + |u| + 1)hv + (n + \tfrac{1}{2})h\omega.$$

(5) Prove that

$$L_n(2x) = n! \sum_{m=0}^{n} \frac{2^{n-m}(-1)^m}{m!(n-m)!} L_{n-m}(x).$$

(6) Prove that

(i) $\dfrac{d}{dx} L_n^m(x) = L_n^{m+1}(x);$

(ii) $L_{n+1}^m(x) + (x - 2n - 1)L_n^m(x) + mL_n^{m-1}(x) + n^2 L_{n-1}^m(x) = 0;$

(iii) $L_n^m(x) - nL_{n-1}^m(x) + nL_{n-1}^{m-1}(x) = 0.$

(7) If $m \leq n$ prove that

$$\int_0^\infty J_m(2\sqrt{x})e^{-x/a}x^{n-\frac{1}{2}m}dx = (-1)^m \frac{(n-m)!}{n!} a^{n+1}e^{-a}L_n^m(a).$$

(8) Prove that if $m \leq n$, $a > 0$,

$$\int_0^\infty e^{-ax}x^m L_n^m(x)dx = \frac{(-1)^m(n!)^2(a-1)^{n-m}}{(n-m)!a^{n+1}},$$

and deduce that if $n \geq l + 1$

$$\int_0^\infty x^{l+1}R_{nl}(x)dx = \frac{\{(n+l)!\}^2}{(n-l-1)!}(-1)^{n+l}2^{2l+2}.$$

(9) Show that

$$\int_0^1 x^m(1-x)^p L_n^m(ax)dx = (-1)^{p+1} \frac{(n!)^2 p!}{\{(n+p)!\}^2} L_{n+p+1}^{m+p+1}(a).$$

(10) Prove that the function

$$x^{\frac{1}{2}\gamma}e^{-\frac{1}{2}x}L_{\alpha+\beta}^{\alpha}(x)$$

is a solution of the differential equation

$$\frac{d^2y}{dx^2} + \frac{\alpha-\gamma+1}{x}\frac{dy}{dx} + \left\{-\frac{1}{4} + \frac{2\beta+\alpha+1}{2x} - \frac{\gamma(2\alpha-\gamma)}{4x^2}\right\}y = 0.$$

(11) The potential energy for the nuclear motion of a diatomic molecule is closely approximated by the Morse function

$$V(r) = De^{-2ar} - 2De^{-ar}.$$

Show that the spherically symmetrical solutions of the Schrödinger equation with this potential are

$$\psi(r) = \frac{C_n}{r}\{\exp(-be^{-ar})\}(2br)^{k-n-\frac{1}{2}}L_{2k-n-1}^{2k-2j-1}(2be^{-ar}),$$

$$(0 \leq n \leq k-\tfrac{1}{2}),$$

where $b = 2\pi(2mD)/(ah)$, C_n is a normalisation constant, and the corresponding values of the energy are

$$W = -D\left[1 - \frac{(n+\frac{1}{2})}{b} + \frac{(n+\frac{1}{2})^2}{4b^2}\right].$$

(12) Prove that the normalisation constant C_n in the previous example has the value

$$\sqrt{\frac{2ba}{N_n}},$$

where

$$N_n = \{\Gamma(2b-n)\}^2 \sum_{r=0}^n \frac{\Gamma(2b-2n+r-1)}{r!}.$$

(13) Show that in parabolic coordinates ξ, η, ϕ defined by the equations

$$x = (\xi\eta)^{\frac{1}{2}}\cos\phi, \quad y = (\xi\eta)^{\frac{1}{2}}\sin\phi, \quad z = \tfrac{1}{2}(\xi-\eta)$$

Schrödinger's equation for a hydrogen-like atom of nuclear charge Ze takes the form

$$\frac{\partial}{\partial\xi}\left(\xi\frac{\partial\psi}{\partial\xi}\right) + \frac{\partial}{\partial\eta}\left(\eta\frac{\partial\psi}{\partial\eta}\right) + \frac{1}{4}\left(\frac{1}{\xi}+\frac{1}{\eta}\right)\frac{\partial^2\psi}{\partial\phi^2}$$

$$+ \frac{2\pi^2 m}{h^2}\{W(\xi+\eta)+2Ze^2\}\psi = 0.$$

Show that this equation has solutions of the form

$$\psi(\xi, \eta, \phi) = C\left(\frac{\xi\eta}{n^2a^2}\right)e^{iu\phi-(\xi+\eta)/2na}L_{k+u}^{u}\left(\frac{\xi}{na}\right)L_{l+u}^{u}\left(\frac{\eta}{na}\right)$$

where a is the Bohr radius, $n = k+l+a+1$ and $W = -2\pi^2 me^4 z^2/(n^2h^2)$.

Determine the constant C so that ψ is normalised to unity.

(14) In the theory of the rotation and vibration spectrum of a diatomic molecule there arises the problem of solving the Schrödinger equation with potential energy

$$V(r) = \frac{B}{r^2} - \frac{Ze^2}{r}.$$

Show that the energy levels are given by

$$W = -2\pi^2 mZ^2e^4/(h^2\sigma^2)$$

where $\sigma = n+\frac{1}{2}+\sqrt{\{b+(l+\frac{1}{2})^2\}}$ with n, l integers and $b = 8\pi^2 mB/h^2$, and that the corresponding wave functions are

$$C_{n\alpha}\left(\frac{2r}{\sigma a}\right)^{\frac{1}{2}\alpha-\frac{1}{2}}e^{-r/\sigma a}L_{n+\alpha}^{\alpha}\left(\frac{2r}{\sigma a}\right)P_l^u(\cos\theta)ei^{u\phi},$$

where a is the Bohr radius, $\alpha = 2\sqrt{\{b+(l+\frac{1}{2})^2\}}$ and $C_{n\alpha}$ is a normalisation factor.

(15) Show that the constant $C_{n\alpha}$ occurring in the last example has the value

$$\left\{ \frac{2}{\sigma a \Gamma(n+\alpha+1)} \right\}^{\frac{1}{2}} \left\{ \frac{(2l+1)n!(l-u)!}{4\pi(2n+\alpha+1)(l+u)!} \right\}^{\frac{1}{2}}.$$

(16) If

$$I(l; n; s) = \int_0^\infty x^{s+2} \{R_{nl}(x)\}^2 dx,$$

prove that $I(l; n; s) \div \{(n+l)!\}^2$ is the coefficient of $(t\tau)^{n+1}$ in the expansion of

$$(1-t)^{s+1}(1-\tau)^{s+1} \sum_r \frac{(2l+s+r+2)!}{r!} (t\tau)^{2l+r+1}.$$

Deduce that

$$I(l; n; -1) = \frac{\{(n+l)!\}^3}{(n-l-1)!},$$

$$I(l; n; 1) = \frac{\{(n+l)!\}^3}{(n-l-1)!} \{6n^2 - 2l(l+1)\}.$$

(17) Show that in a hydrogen-like atom of nuclear charge Ze the average distance of the electron from the nucleus, in the state described by quantum numbers l, n, is

$$\frac{n^2 a}{Z} \left[1 + \frac{1}{2} \left\{ 1 - \frac{l(l+1)}{n^2} \right\} \right].$$

Find the average value of $1/r$ and show that the total energy of a hydrogen atom is just one-half of the average potential energy.

THE DIRAC DELTA FUNCTION

§ **46. The Dirac delta function.** In mathematical physics we often encounter functions which have non-zero values in very short intervals. For example, an impulsive force is envisaged as acting for only a very short interval of time. The Dirac delta function, which is used extensively in quantum mechanics and classical applied mathematics, may be thought of as a generalisation of this concept.

If we consider the function

$$\delta_a(x) = \begin{cases} \dfrac{1}{2a}, & |x| < a; \\ 0, & |x| > a, \end{cases} \tag{46.1}$$

then it is readily shown that

$$\int_{-\infty}^{\infty} \delta_a(x)dx = 1. \tag{46.2}$$

Also, if $f(x)$ is any function which is integrable in the interval $(-a, a)$ then, by using the mean value theorem of the integral calculus, we see that

$$\int_{-\infty}^{\infty} f(x)\delta_a(x)dx = \frac{1}{2a} \int_{-a}^{a} f(x)dx = f(\theta a), \quad |\theta| \leqq 1. \tag{46.3}$$

We now define

$$\delta(x) = \lim_{a \to 0} \delta_a(x). \tag{46.4}$$

Letting a tend to zero in equations (46.1) and (46.2) we

see that $\delta(x)$ satisfies the relations

$$\delta(x) = 0, \text{ if } x \neq 0, \qquad (46.5)$$

$$\int_{-\infty}^{\infty} \delta(x)dx = 1. \qquad (46.6)$$

The " function " $\delta(x)$, defined by equations (46.5) and (46.6), is known as the Dirac delta function. It is unlike the functions we normally encounter in mathematics; the latter are defined to have a definite value (or values) at each point of a certain domain. For this reason Dirac has called the delta function an " improper function " and has emphasised that it may be used in mathematical analysis only when no inconsistency can possibly arise from its use. The delta function could be dispensed with entirely by using a limiting procedure involving ordinary functions of the kind $\delta_a(x)$, but the " function " $\delta(x)$ and its " derivatives " play such a useful role in the formulation and solution of boundary value problems in classical mathematical physics as well as in quantum mechanics that it is important to derive the formal properties of the Dirac delta function. It should be emphasised, however, that these properties are purely formal.

First of all it should be observed that the precise variation of $\delta(x)$ in the neighbourhood of the origin is not important provided that its oscillations, if it has any, are not too violent. For instance, the function

$$\delta(x) = \lim_{n \to \infty} \frac{\sin(2\pi nx)}{\pi x}$$

satisfies the equations (46.5) and (46.6) and has the same formal properties as the function defined by equation (46.4).

If we let a tend to zero in equation (46.3) we obtain the relation

$$\int_{-\infty}^{\infty} f(x)\delta(x)dx = f(0), \qquad (46.7)$$

which a simple change of variable transforms to

$$\int_{-\infty}^{\infty} f(x)\delta(x-a)dx = f(a). \qquad (46.8)$$

In other words the operation of multiplying $f(x)$ by $\delta(x-a)$ and integrating over all x is merely equivalent to substituting a for x in the original function. Symbolically we may write

$$f(x)\delta(x-a) = f(a)\delta(x-a) \qquad (46.9)$$

if we remember that this equation has a meaning only in the sense that its two sides give equivalent results when used as factors in an integrand. As a special case we have

$$x\delta(x) = 0. \qquad (46.10)$$

In a similar way we can prove the relations

$$\delta(-x) = \delta(x), \qquad (46.11)$$

$$\delta(ax) = \frac{1}{a}\,\delta(x), \quad a > 0, \qquad (46.12)$$

$$\delta(a^2 - x^2) = \frac{1}{2a}\{\delta(x-a) + \delta(x+a)\}, \quad a > 0. \qquad (46.13)$$

Let us now consider the interpretation we must put upon the " derivatives " of $\delta(x)$. If we assume that $\delta'(x)$ exists and that both it and $\delta(x)$ can be regarded as ordinary functions in the rule for integrating by parts we see that

$$\int_{-\infty}^{\infty} f(x)\delta'(x)dx = \left[f(x)\delta(x) \right]_{-\infty}^{\infty}$$
$$- \int_{-\infty}^{\infty} f'(x)\delta(x)dx = -f'(0).$$

Repeating this process we find that

$$\int_{-\infty}^{\infty} f(x)\delta^{(n)}(x)dx = (-1)^n f^{(n)}(0). \qquad (46.14)$$

The statement is often made that the Dirac delta function is the derivative of the Heaviside unit function $H(x)$ defined by the equations

$$H(x) = \begin{cases} 1, & \text{if } x > 0; \\ 0, & \text{if } x < 0; \end{cases}$$

and it is easy to see on geometrical grounds that there are reasons for conjecturing such a relationship. To make it precise we note that if, in the definition † of the Stieltjes integral

$$\int_{-\infty}^{\infty} f(x)\,dF(x),$$

we take $F(x)$ to be the Heaviside function $H(x)$, we find immediately that, for any integrable function $f(x)$,

$$\int_{-\infty}^{\infty} f(x)\,dH(x) = f(0). \tag{46.15}$$

Comparing equation (46.15) with equation (46.7) we see the relation between $H(x)$ and $\delta(x)$. It may be seen from these equations that $\delta(x)$ is not a function but a Stieltjes measure, and that the use of the Dirac delta function could be avoided entirely by a systematic use of Stieltjes integration.

† The simplest definition of a Stieltjes integral $\int_{b}^{a} f(x)\,dF(x)$ is as the limit of approximative sums $\Sigma f(\xi_r)[F(x_r) - F(x_{r-1})]$, where the x_r, the points of subdivision of (a, b) and ξ_r, lies in the interval (x_{r-1}, x_r).

INDEX